Teaching Science
in the
Elementary School

Teaching Science
in the
Elementary School

116487

DAVID P. BUTTS

Professor of Curriculum and Instruction
Science Education Center
The University of Texas at Austin

THE FREE PRESS
A Division of Macmillan Publishing Co., Inc.
NEW YORK
Collier Macmillan Publishers
LONDON

A Division of Macmillan Publishing Co., Inc.

The Free Press
A Division of Macmillan Publishing Co., Inc.
866 Third Avenue, New York, New York 10022

Collier-Macmillan Canada Ltd.

Library of Congress Catalog Card Number: 72-86790

Printed in the United States of America

printing number

3   4   5   6   7   8   9   10

To Velma

Preface

This book is designed for one purpose: to focus your attention on teaching science to children.

Teaching can be described as an act which has two scenes. The first scene includes those deliberate steps taken in planning and implementing learning experiences; the second scene involves the spontaneous interaction of the child with the learning experience. Both of these scenes must be incorporated within a teacher's frame of reference for a learning experience to be successful. The spontaneous interaction of the child is *part of the preparation* for the next experience and *must* take place. Either phase of teaching without the other is of no value whatsoever.

The main concern of this book is to analyze these two scenes. Throughout these pages you will find many classroom episodes which illustrate both phases of teaching. These are experiences that teachers have shared during the past several years in using the new science curriculum materials. They are all real experiences which serve to highlight the principles embodied in this book. By analyzing the episodes, you will be able to compare and contrast alternative teaching strategies and evaluate their effectiveness in terms of changes in the behavior of the children.

I am indebted to many colleagues and associates who have provided the extensive body of knowledge from which I have drawn so freely. It is not feasible at this time to list the many teachers from whom I have gleaned ideas and to whom I am grateful for their influence on my thinking. Although I accept full responsibility for any deficiencies this text may have, credit for its strengths must certainly be shared with the many who have helped shape these ideas.

David P. Butts
Austin, Texas

Editor's Introduction

Countless man hours and hundreds of thousands of dollars have been devoted in recent years to efforts to improve science instruction in the schools. Much of the effort has been focused on development of new and better curriculums and materials. Leading scholars both in learning theory and in the sciences have developed new science programs for elementary schools. Three of the more significant programs, developed in the 1960s with National Science Foundation support, are presented in this book. Along with descriptions of these programs—Elementary Science Study (ESS), Science Curriculum Improvement Study (SCIS), and *Science—A Process Approach* (AAAS)—Professor David Butts offers concrete suggestions for effective use of the materials.

Even though science educators have high regard for the new programs, they are not widely and effectively used in the elementary schools. As a matter of fact, the vast majority of those teaching science still rely heavily on conventional textbooks.

A primary reason teachers, especially beginners, rely so heavily on "textbook teaching" is that they have not been prepared to use new programs and materials, new teaching strategies and techniques. Pedantic, abstract, and second-hand teaching methodology is characteristic of too many methods books and courses in preservice education programs. Books in the *Introduction to Teaching* series seek to meaningfully relate subject matter and pedagogy. Both are essential for successful teaching. Methods courses should help prospective teachers to achieve understanding of subject matter and to develop skills and techniques of teaching. Both "achieve" and "develop" are active verbs. They denote student and teacher involvement.

Teacher involvement in the selection of subject matter to be learned and in the development of instructional materials has been a crucial missing ingredient in most efforts to improve science education. In *Teaching Science in the Elementary School,* Professor Butts seeks to supply the missing ingredient. He has prepared a textbook for courses in the teaching of science that is both a source of content or subject matter and of suggested teaching and learning processes which vitally involve both the teacher and the child. Professor Butts has presented and illustrated ways for the teacher to produce and use his or her own materials and teaching techniques as well as those in the aforementioned new programs. Of equal importance pedagogically, due cognizance has been taken of the child's role in teaching and learning processes.

A key to understanding and effective use of *Teaching Science in the Elementary School* is provided in the first chapter. That key is the concept of teaching which gives direction to the book. Teaching is defined to include subject matter, experience of both the teacher and the child, and the nature and consequences of learning. Thus, modern science instruction is conceived and presented as a merging of concepts, materials, processes, and human experience—all of which are vehicles for teaching and learning.

This book has the tone of authenticity and practicality throughout. There is a ready explanation of the presence of the tone. Professor Butts is himself an accomplished teacher. He has developed many of the materials in real elementary classrooms with real children. He has witnessed and evaluated the episodes he uses so effectively in the book. In different types of schools, he has supervised and evaluated implementation of new programs described. He has used the material in this book in his teaching of science education courses at the University of Texas. In short, this book is the product of a practitioner as well as a scholar.

Teaching of Science in the Elementary School should be useful to professors of science education and to prospective elementary teachers in methods courses. It should be valuable also to experienced teachers as well as science supervisors in elementary schools.

B. J. Chandler, Dean
School of Education
Northwestern University

Contents

Teaching Science
in the
Elementary School

A Decision
Framework for
Facilitating
Individual
Learning

CHAPTER 1

What Does It Mean to Teach Science? A Personal Frame of Reference

If you found a man hungry and gave him a fish,
　　you have fed him for a day.
If you gave him a pole and let him "discover with it,"
　　you may or may not have helped him (you may get
　　clubbed).
If you gave him a pole and taught him how to use it,
　　you may have fed him for a lifetime.

TO TEACH

Words are a significant means by which we communicate ideas. Words, however, have different meanings. The meaning any word has for an individual is directly related to his past experience as well as to the concept which the word is describing. Past experiences vary among children and adults, and between them the use of a single word may evoke quite different mental images. Consider, for example, the contrasts in mental images possible to a six-year-old and his teacher in this statement: "The carpenter put the board on the horse and began to saw."

Because meanings vary, it is essential in discussing the topic, "What Teaching Science Means to You," that we share a common definition of the word "teaching."

In this teaching–learning episode, underline those phrases that you think are part of "teaching."

Episode 1.1

With a group of active sixth-graders, Mrs. B. was concerned about their ability to identify the important variables in a system. One morning, as they arrived in the classroom, the children observed on the center table a large dishpan of water and a square plastic refrigerator container with strings attached. To start the class, Mrs. B. asked the children to watch the plastic container, which she placed in the water. Then, using the strings, she lifted the container out. The suspended vessel began to move clockwise as water came out four holes in its sides. The holes had been drilled near the bottom on each side of the container. When the water had nearly all run out, the children observed that the container stopped moving in a clockwise direction and began to rotate in a counter-clockwise direction.

The class was grouped with four children at each table. Mrs. B. asked each group to write down two questions about what they had observed. The class shared these questions and noted that fourteen different questions were asked. They agreed on which question would be pursued first. That question was: "Why did the bucket move in one direction and then change and move in a different direction?"

One class member was selected to serve as a "chalkboard recorder." Various children identified specific parts of the system which they thought related in some way to the question. As items were being listed, some in the class were quite vocal, questioning whether children's contributions were really observations or not. If the child could defend his comment, it was listed. If not, he agreed to wait for the present time. For a few minutes, this discussion and sharing of ideas continued. The list on the board included: water, plastic container, holes on each side, more than one hole, string, power to lift the string, color of container, amount of water in container.

Mrs. B. then asked the class to identify one or two parts of the system as most closely related to the reason for the direction of the motion of the container. Most of the class identified water and holes as the most important factors. Their task was then to design a way to test if and how the water and holes were related to the motion of the container. Three of the six groups were asked to investigate the water variable, and the other three groups were to inquire about the hole variable.

The "water group" decided that, to really test the effect of water on the motion of the container, they would have to use a container like the one used in the initial activity. They could then lift the container out of different substances: cooking oil, alcohol, air, and Karo syrup. These are known to flow at different rates. Several days later, this group reported to the class that their container moved clockwise and then counter-clockwise with water, alcohol, and cooking oil. It moved only slightly with air and not at all with Karo syrup. Their conclusion was that, in order to make the container move, the contents had to run out through the holes and push in some way to start the container moving. They also wondered about the container of air moving, concluding that it did so because of the twist of the string. They added another conclusion that since the container moved clockwise and counter-clockwise with water, alcohol, and oil, the kind of liquid really did not make a difference.

The "container hole" group was puzzled as to how to get started. Mrs. B. sat down with them and asked what puzzled them. One child said, "Well, how do you investigate a hole? It's either there or it's not there." Another quickly replied, "That's it! Let's do it with a container with no holes and see if it works."

The group was ready for action when Mrs. B. stopped them with one question: "What are you going to look for?" Her question didn't seem to communicate, so she asked another: "How will you know if the holes or no holes make a difference?" They quickly agreed that the answer to that question would be in the observation of the clockwise and counter-clockwise motion of the container. The children observed a container with holes and another without holes and determined that the one with holes moved as expected, but the container without holes did not move. The group felt they were ready to report back when one child wondered if they had really answered the question: "Why did the container move in one direction and then in another?" Would the container move, for example, if it had only one hole or if all four holes were on one side? This quickly added alternatives as to the number, location, and size of the holes. Several days later, the "container hole" group reported their conclusions: that the placement of the holes in the container was the real reason for the motion. Mrs. B. found that when she questioned them further, no one in the group had given any thought to why the placement of holes was important.

Analysis of Episode 1.1

In this teaching episode, how many sentences that you underlined were also underlined by at least three others?

Which ones did only you underline?

In reflecting about the entire episode, how would it have been different if there had been no teacher?

How would it have been different if no children were present?

Who was doing the learning?

You might find it very useful now to write your definition of teaching before you continue to read this chapter.

DEFINING TEACHING

What does teaching mean to you? To define it, what actions would you expect from a person who was teaching that would distinguish him from a person who was not teaching?

To teach, does one have to have 32 children seated at desks arranged in rows? Does one have to have 20 children? Four children? Any children?

To teach, does one have to be talking, lecturing, demonstrating, reading, or writing on the chalkboard? To teach, must one have a textbook, lesson plans, or lecture notes? To teach, does one sit or stand, use a lectern, or walk around the room?

Answers to each of these questions will largely depend upon what kind of a concept of teaching we have. And our concept will be based on our past experiences.

That concepts of teaching vary is illustrated by a dictionary definition which says that to teach is to give a lesson, or to show how to do, to provide with knowledge, or to guide the study of. "Teaching" is usually used in one of three ways: (1) It may be used to refer to what is taught as a doctrine or body of knowledge. Thus, the "teachings of the church" refers to a body of ideas or systems of a belief. (2) "Teaching" may refer to an occupation or a profession. This describes what you do for a living. (3) "Teaching" may be used to describe ways of making something known to others or sharing with them, usually in the routine of an organized school.

Teaching can thus be defined in terms of subject matter: "Teaching is the act of providing certain knowledge." When observing a "teaching" situation, one could evaluate how much teaching has gone on by determining how much knowledge has been provided. Specific tests of knowledge are usually used as evidence that the knowledge has been provided; hence, teaching has occurred.

To some, however, past experience rejects a definition of teaching in terms of subject matter; it seems inadequate. Their past experience includes situations which they want to term as "teaching," but in which the measurable amounts of subject matter may not have been impressive. What was more vivid was the action of the teacher. Hence, a second definition: "Teaching is what the teacher does; one giving a lesson or showing how to do something." Using this definition, evaluation of teaching suggests that one look for variety in the actions of the teacher.

For some, however, the definition of teaching as being that which the teacher does is once again too limited. Teaching could be done whether children were present or absent. To some, then, teaching is defined as what the child does, or according to Webster's definition: "teaching is guiding the student in his study of science." This definition would imply that one must look for situations in which children are assisted in discovering and confronting meaningful experiences which confuse, puzzle, or intrigue them.

If definitions are built from past experience, they describe part of a reality. The three blind men of Hindustan reported their observations. Each of their descriptions of the elephant was accurate for what each was describing. In a similar way, each of these three definitions of teaching includes relevant aspects of teaching but is incomplete in itself. For our discussion, we will use the following definition of teaching: "Teaching is what one person does to another in using an experience or situation to increase the second person's perception or understanding of that experience." Teaching thus includes the subject matter (the experience), what the teacher does (what one does to another), and that which results (increased perception or understanding). While teaching describes an action of the teacher, implied in the definition of teaching is an outcome of the act of teaching—the child learns.

Consider, for example, in the next two episodes, how these teachers helped children learn.

Episode 1.2

Mrs. H. had rearranged her class for variety. The 29 children in her third-grade class were arranged in five rows with six children in each (and one seat empty). During her science period, Mrs. H. had emphasized the importance of children grouping objects and then telling their reasons for thinking that the objects belonged together. Several of the children had volunteered to separate their classmates into groups, and others had identified the reasons for these groupings. One child had put three boys in one group and three girls in another group. The class quickly determined that number wasn't the reason since there was the same number of members in each set. The reason for grouping was boys or girls. A second child then put four boys and girls in one group. Since obviously boys or girls could not be the basis for the grouping, the class looked for another reason. They identified the reason— all the children were wearing green. Several others constructed groups based on color of cloth, types of shoes, color of hair or eyes, and other distinctions.

George was then asked to make a group. He called out five

boys and said they all belonged together for a special reason. Suggestions from the class included many ideas, but they either didn't fit each of the five boys or were not George's reason. Finally, the class and Mrs. H. gave up. George then pointed to where the boys had been sitting and explained the way in which the five boys were grouped was that they sat in a diagonal line across the classroom.

Analysis of Episode 1.2

Which definition of teaching best fits Mrs. H.'s actions here?

What is the reason for your choice?

In what way would the situation have been different if Mrs. H. were not present?

In the next episode, contrast Mr. J.'s action with that of Mrs. H.

Episode 1.3

Mr. J. was concerned with the accuracy with which his fifth-grade class distinguished between mass and weight. Most of the class had good reading achievement scores. He checked several science texts located in the classroom and decided that two of them had good reference materials that made distinctions between mass and weight. When his class returned from the music period, they found a science assignment on the chalkboard. It directed them to read chapters from the two texts and then answer these two questions: (1) Write a definition of mass. (2) Write a definition of weight.

About 30 minutes later, Mr. J. observed that most of his class had finished their science assignment. He called on three of the children to read their definitions. Most of the rest of the class agreed that the definitions were satisfactory. Mr. J. then asked everyone to put their definitions in their science notebooks. After the usual snapping of notebook covers and tearing of paper, he observed with satisfaction that most of the children knew where to find the science notebooks and had followed his directions.

That task completed, the students began their math lesson.

Analysis of Episode 1.3

What definition of teaching best fits Mr. J.'s actions here?

What is the reason for your choice?

DEFINING LEARNING

How do you determine whether an individual has "learned?" To answer this question, a definition of "learning" would be useful. Obviously, one must first specify what is to be learned. A definition could therefore be a description of subject matter. He is learning biology. She is learning parts of a flower. He is learning to define a system.

When a person has learned, measuring thus becomes a task of observing him name the parts of a flower or relate the definition of a system. However, if learning is the outcome of teaching, how does the teacher determine whether a child's ability to name the parts of a flower results from his teaching or from knowledge the child brought to the classroom from another source?

Another description of learning can be based on changes which occur in the child. Learning is the acquisition of specific behavioral characteristics. To determine whether or not a child learned parts of the flower, you would (a) find out what parts of the flower the child could name, (b) direct the child's preception of the flower by using a specific experience, and (c) identify which parts of the flower the child could name in a new situation.

The result of teaching, and the means by which one can decide if teaching has occurred, is the change in the behavior of the child.

USING DEFINITIONS OF TEACHING–LEARNING

A definition seems to suggest that the "definition" itself is useful for something. The implication of the definitions of teaching and learning is that the child is actively involved in his learning experience and that his behavior is being changed because of his learning experiences—in these examples, in science.

In the following teaching–learning episodes, identify and describe the child behavior *changes* that are illustrated.

Episode 1.4

A first-grade teacher was assigned to a group of 27 children. Most of these children came from homes where the conversation was in Spanish rather than English. The teacher was familiar with the background of the children and recognized that not only was the school a new experience for the child, it was also a world in which the language, English, was a new experience.

To this teacher, "science" means emphasizing the child's ability to both point out and describe various experiences in such a way that others would clearly know what he was saying. She had chosen a series of experiences in which the children were identifying and naming two- and three-dimensional shapes they observed in objects around the room.

Nearly two months later, two very excited children came to the teacher. "Oh, Miss C., there's a big circle out there." When the teacher followed them out to the school playground, she saw road machinery at work on the street in front of the school. Several children were clustered at the fence near where the machine was slowly moving over the rough gravel. Several quickly identified the shape like a circle on the large rear wheels. Then one child, Ramon, pointed out the cylinder. When Miss C. asked him which it was, he responded, "the part that makes the ground go flat."

Analysis of Episode 1.4

What evidence did Miss C. have that the children had acquired some behavioral change; that is, learned from their science experiences?

What specific actions of Miss C. illustrate your definition of teaching?

Episode 1.5

Mrs. D. had a class of 31 first-graders who seemed especially immature, even for six-year-old children. They followed class routine only with great difficulty. In addition to their immaturity, most of the class seemed to have had few experiences that prepared them for school work. With the time pressure in achieving the other tasks that first grade must accomplish, science teaching was a real problem for Mrs. D. For young children, she decided that helping them to describe their experiences in unambiguous language would not only help the children with their science competencies but also in other areas such as reading. Mrs. D. used several activities to introduce the names of two- and three-dimensional shapes. She also had many activities in which the children practiced using the names of these shapes to describe objects. In one activity, the children constructed a castle that included objects shaped like circles, triangles, squares, rectangles, and elipses; also cones, cylinders, spheres, elipsoids, and rectangular parallelepipeds.

About a month after the introduction of these tools for describing, Mrs. D. watched the boys and girls at lunch. At one of the tables there seemed to be an active debate. Mrs. D. moved closer to listen. The debate centered on whether they were eating cubes and spheres or cubes and elipsoids for lunch. Smiling to herself at the carrots and peas on the plates, Mrs. D. then asked if anybody saw a shape like a circle. Several pointed to the plates on the trays. Mrs. D. said that she also saw a shape like a rectangle. One of the boys replied, "Oh, no, Mrs. D., it's a rectangular parallelepiped." It was, for she had been pointing to fish sticks on their plates. Mrs. D. glowed with pleasure. Her children were demonstrating that they had learned!

Analysis of Episode 1.5

What evidence does Mrs. D. have to say that her children had learned?

What actions of Mrs. D. illustrate your definition of teaching?

Episode 1.6

In a third-grade class, Mrs. G. noticed that Elizabeth had difficulty with most of her school work except science. Science to Mrs. G. was a time when children had the opportunity to organize information from their experiences and to share this with other boys and girls in the class. Elizabeth seemed to really shine when given the opportunity. For example, one day Mrs. G. had the children playing a "can you guess" game. In this game, the leader made two groups of objects or children. In both groups, each object or child was alike in some manner but different from children or objects in the other group. For example, one group of books was all science books and the other group of books was all not science books.

Elizabeth was a leader in this particular game. She had placed four boys in one group and five boys in a second group. The rest of the class attempted to guess what was the reason for the two groups. Finally, they gave up and turned to Mrs. G. Mrs. G. had been carefully studying the two groups and was genuinely puzzled. She could find no respect in which the four boys were like each other but different from the other group of five boys.

She also gave up and asked Elizabeth for her secret. With a great deal of delight, Elizabeth grinned, exhibiting four missing teeth, as she pointed out that the four boys were all wearing belts and the five boys in the other group were not wearing belts!

Analysis of Episode 1.6

What evidence did Mrs. G. have that Elizabeth was involved in this learning experience?

SUMMARY

An outline of the task to be done permits each individual to identify smaller parts of the task that fit together and to explain how. Science experiences are part of the total task because of the opportunities they provide for students to learn. For a child to learn, his teacher must be an essential contributor in many situations. Operational definitions of both learning and teaching thus provide us with an outline of the task for which we are concerned—teaching science.

Learning is defined here as acquiring behavioral change.

Many definitions of teaching could be included. Each would include those aspects of our past experience that we identify as related to what teaching is: To some, teaching is designing; to others it is drilling, or enlightening, giving instruction, lecturing, indoctrinating, instilling, training, or tutoring. All these terms could be relevant. The definition that is related to science teaching which has been suggested here is: teaching is defined as what a teacher does to facilitate learning or the acquisition of behavioral change.

Consequently, teaching is the removing of roadblocks to learning behavior acquisitions—a facilitator of learning rather than a hindrance.

SHARPENING YOUR DEFINITION OF TEACHING

In these selections you will find authors describing problems of teachers who face obstacles to learning. You may find in them a challenge to your own view of teaching. They will help you rethink the vital foundations for your success in teaching.

Friedman, Frederica. "The Boundaries of Elementary School Science." *Science and Children,* April 1968, pp. 31–32.

Science includes a tremendously wide range of possibilities for classroom instruction. Ultimately, the teacher must select—but on what basis? In this article you will find one basis described with which you can compare your own rationale.

LeBoeuf, Flores. "Qui Docet Discit—He Who Teaches, Learns." *The Science Teacher,* January 1968, pp. 53–56.

This interesting article describes what one teacher did to cope with the problem of the uninvolved child. The results of giving children the status and responsibility of teaching will amaze you.

CHAPTER FOCUS

1. Write one or two sentences that you think express the central idea of Chapter 1.

2. Review the list of suggested central ideas. Identify those that are most like yours, and those that are least like yours. State the reasons for the similarities and differences.

Suggested Central Ideas

1. Perhaps the central task was to have me ask myself what my honest reactions really are to each of the situations. Is this way or that way of teaching really best, and why?

2. A central task was to read some of the definitions and think if and how they are applicable to teaching situations; and, thus, make an honest evaluation of how and what I teach.

3. Teaching is the removal of obstacles that result in behavioral change in children.

4. When teaching science or any subject, I, as the teacher, am in the role of director or guide in which I structure experiences, and in which the learner has the first-hand experience and comes to his own conclusions rather than just mine. It is also important that the director lends a helping hand or creates the opportunity in which the learner does the best that he can.

5. Teaching science means that I should structure a problem which frees the child to question the experiment, observe, and even fail, always noting the change in the behavior of the child.

6. Teaching science is a process in which the child acquires a desired behavioral change through some action on my part.

7. After considering separate examples of widely different approaches I might use in teaching science, I evaluate each situation and decide which were successful. In the Summary, it is stated what teaching means to the author; now I can decide if and how I agree or disagree with the author's conclusion.

8. As in any learning, science learning takes place only when a "roadblock" is encountered in teaching, and I, as the teacher, help to remove that obstacle. It is implied that the discovery method is involved.

CHAPTER 2

What Should I Teach?
Selecting Ideas

Teaching science was defined as removing roadblocks to learning, and facilitating the child as he acquires changes in behavior. Deciding which roadblocks should be removed is an essential decision for science teachers. Determining what to teach in science is like asking the question, "On my trip, where should I go?" The answer depends upon: (1) where do I want to go? (2) how much time do I have? (3) how much money do I have?

In making decisions about instruction in science, factors such as these must also be considered: (1) what are the instructional objectives? (2) how and what roadblocks seem to exist? (3) how much time is available for instruction in science to remove these roadblocks? (4) what are my previous experiences in the area of science in helping children to identify roadblocks and facilitate their removal? (5) what interest do I have in this area of science? (6) what science areas are related to the "behavior roadblock"?

The answer to the question, "What Should I Teach?," requires decisions to be made about the removal of specific roadblocks. In Episodes 2.1 and 2.2, the behavior of the teachers illustrates their answers to this question. In each episode, the teacher makes decisions about what science to teach. You will find it useful to list the factors that help form that teacher's decisions.

Episode 2.1

Mrs. M. was planning the first science unit for her third-grade class. Just prior to school, she had received the cumulative folders on the 34 children who were to be in her class. The records seemed to indicate that she would have a class of above-average children who had encountered some limited experiences in science. Based on what she had done in the two previous years, she thought that a unit using the aquarium would be a good beginning one. Last year, her children were really enthusiastic in their interest about the aquarium, and the device offered so many possibilities, not only in science, but in correlated activities in art and language. The boys and girls could draw pictures of the aquarium for their science notebook covers; they could do several creative writing stories during the aquarium "study." As she continued her planning, Mrs. M. listed the important parts of the aquarium and the animals and plants she would need. She remembered that, last year, there were several words the children needed to understand, such as evaporation, gravid and non-gravid, reptiles, mammals, amphibians, and photosynthesis. An attractive bulletin board with each of these words and its definition would help the children, Mrs. M. concluded. Then there were the scientific names of the animals and plants. These could be listed on a worksheet; the children could draw pictures of the plant or animal beside each name. Mrs. M. smiled at this second opportunity for correlation of science activities with art. As she thought of the plants, she was reminded of the possibility of a film on photosynthesis. That might fit very well into the discussion on the plants in the aquarium.

By this time, Mrs. M. had blocked out the following schedule:

Monday	Introduce study; review the bulletin board.
Tuesday	Set up the aquarium and have children make notebook covers.
Wednesday	Write a creative story about yesterday's aquarium encounter.
Thursday	Worksheet on the parts of the aquarium.
Friday	Worksheet on scientific names of plants and animals. Draw pictures of each.
Monday	Discuss evaporation of water in aquarium as part of the water cycle. Point out the words on the bulletin board.

Tuesday	Film on photosynthesis.
Wednesday	Discuss plant growth.
Thursday	Sharing of experiences with the aquarium.
Friday	Unit evaluation.

Episode 2.2

Mrs. S. was also preparing her first day with a new third-grade class. She reviewed the available information about the children. They appeared to be alert, interested children who gave no evidence of serious learning difficulty. Knowing the importance of having activities in all subject areas that both interest and involve the students from the beginning, she decided to use an aquarium. Her reason for selecting it from the various possibilities available was that she wanted to know how well her children could observe a system, distinguish between parts of a system, construct a grouping, and defend their choice on the objects in the grouping. The aquarium fit these goals rather well.

To begin the study, Mrs. S. decided to have the aquarium in the room set up, but without the fish or plants. After the first day (in which she would not say anything about the aquarium), she would add plants to the system. Then on Wednesday, the third day, she could have the children describe what they had observed on Monday and Tuesday. This would give her an opportunity to identify those in the group who were keen observers. As part of this period, Mrs. S. planned to have various children share their experiences in keeping an aquarium. Wednesday evening she planned to add the fish. Deciding which fish she would purchase was made easier by knowing that the reason for adding fish was to assist children in grouping objects. She would need two or three fish of each of three or four different kinds or groups.

The next day the children would list all the things in the aquarium. This list might include such things as air filter, goldfish, black mollies, water, rock, plants, sand, turtle, turtle float, shells, and so on.

Mrs. S. would then ask the children to group all the objects on their lists into two groups and to tell the reason for their groups.

This task would be followed by continued work on sub-grouping of the items in the initial list, until a complete classification system could be constructed. An appraisal sheet was planned on which the children would build a classification system for a group of books in their reading corner. In building her plan, Mrs. S. reviewed several films, filmstrips, transparencies, and library books. She selected those she thought would provide additional insights about observable characteristics of the parts of the aquarium and, so, would assist children in constructing their classification system.

Analysis of Episodes 2.1 and 2.2

1. In comparing the two episodes, which factors influenced the teacher on the topic for the first study?

2. Compare the basis each teacher had for deciding which experiences to include in the unit.

3. Each teacher had to decide what materials were to be used. What was the basis of the decision for Mrs. M.? for Mrs. S.?

4. References were selected for use by the children in both studies. Contrast the function of reference in each case.

5. What specific results did Mrs. M. expect from the study of the aquarium? Mrs. S.?

6. Compare the evaluative procedures planned by both teachers.

7. How did each teacher decide on which correlated activities to use?

"What should I teach" is a question that requires a specific answer. The answer illustrated by Episodes 2.1 and 2.2 is dependent upon an all-important decision. *What should be taught depends upon what are the expected results of the instruction.* General goals are useful guides toward specific results but are an inadequate basis for deciding what should be taught.

For example, a general goal for a science teacher is that children be able to process the information of their experience. This could be used as a general goal for any science lesson. It offers very little help in making decisions about what should be done as part of a specific science lesson. It will provide no direction for the use of the aquarium in either Episode 2.1 or 2.2.

Specifying the results expected as a result of instruction does offer a clear basis to the teacher for making decisions. An illustration of descriptions of specific results is: "At the end of this study, the children should be able to:

1. Identify and name parts of a system,

2. Distinguish between parts of a system that are very much alike, such as types of fish or plants, and

3. Construct a classification scheme so that an individual part can be identified."

Decision 1.   What are the learning results I want? With the clearly described, expected results, it is possible for the teacher to make a series of decisions about part of the answer to the question, "What should I teach?"

Decision 2.   What topic will facilitate this learning? When one considers such goals as constructing and classifying systems, the choice of topics are many. Aquarium, rocks, color, texture, and plants represent only a few. The decision here is usually made by selecting a topic in which the teacher thinks or assumes the child is interested. Recalling that the object of teaching is learning, and that the learner is the child, it would seem essential that the teacher provide a *selection* of topics, any one of which could be directed toward the needed behavioral change. In addition, topic selection involves identifying those previous experiences essential to the students acquiring the expected results. Choosing a topic depends on the appeal the topic might have for the child, and on the child's previous experience with the topic—a factor essential to the achievement of desired results. To make this decision, one needs to have both a series of alternatives and an insight into children's interests. Topic selection also involves your interest as a teacher and your previous experience in a variety of topics. It is usually most difficult to be enthusiastic about science topics with which you have had no experience. The alternatives need to be those with which you have had enough experience to aid you in guiding the children's activities.

Decision 3.   What types of experiences? There are a variety of experiences possible within any topic. The teacher's task is to identify those experiences which are most likely to facilitate the child in learning how to reach the goals of the study. Reading a book about photosynthesis might be interesting to a child, but it is quite unrelated to constructing a classification scheme. In making such decisions, it is helpful to list all the possible activities, then rate them as to which are most likely to help the child achieve the goals, which may be related to the goals, and which are related to the topic, but not to the goals.

Decision 4.   What materials are needed? With goals, topic, and experience decisions made, material selection becomes a much easier task. In general, the younger the child, the more concrete should be the materials. For a child who has never observed an aquarium, using pictures or even a movie of an aquarium is second-hand experience. Care should be taken in the selection of the materials to insure that the child has first-hand experience before he is expected to use second-hand data.

Decision 5.   What correlated activities could be used? Reinforcement of an idea gained in one experience by the use of that idea in several experiences greatly helps learning. It is important to note that this refers to the *use* of the idea, not just the label for the idea. Correlated activities resulting in the use of an idea are a splendid way in which to reinforce learning. Language development derived from the experience, or art exercises which encourage the use of ideas gained in science are illustrations of such correlation.

Decision 6.   What evaluation? Evaluation of the behavior change in children can only be done when there is a clear definition of what behavior change was expected. In the observation of Episode 2.2, it was not possible to construct a valid evaluation. If, however, one has identified expected effects of the experiences, then the evaluation task is greatly simplified; it means setting for the children some task and then observing the behavior (verbal or written) to see to what extent the children can perform those behaviors described as the expected effects.

SUMMARY

"What should I teach in science?" is a question of early importance to a science teacher. From the wide variety of instructional materials available, there must be some choices made. These decisions require, first, that the teacher identify expected effects of the experience. Based on this decision, the teacher then involves the student in the choice of topics from a series of equally useful alternatives. With an assessment of prerequisite skills, the teacher then can identify or construct specific instructional experiences, select materials and correlated activities, and determine what evaluation experiences will be used.

The aggregate of these decisions represents an answer to the question, "What should I teach?"

SHARPENING YOUR FOCUS ON WHAT YOU SHOULD TEACH

Ashley, James P. "Among the Living." *Science and Children,* November 1967, pp. 34–35.

With a decision about the use of living things, a means to study animal classification, Ashley describes alternatives to the involvement of children with a subject. To what extent were the children's interests involved in these choices? To what extent were the limitations of the teacher's experience a factor in deciding what to use?

Blanc, Sam S. "Creative Thinking for the Process Skills." *Science and Children,* May 1967, pp. 6–7.

According to Blanc, general goals for science instruction provide the basis for decision making in science teaching. What you do depends upon where you are headed. What are the two general goals for science instruction which he describes? Which general goal does the author seem to indicate as his preference? Would he limit his science teaching to these goals? What is the reason for your answer?

Monoszon, E., M. Skatkin, and I. Lerner. "Elementary and Secondary Education." *Soviet Education,* August 17, 1967, pp. 3–6.

As described in this article, one aim of the "modern lesson" is to develop the school children's cognitive interest and abilities and to serve as a major means for their general development. Its task is to teach children to think, judge, establish cause-and-effect relations, and defend their opinions. To a large extent, the richness and imagination and development of the memory and speech of school children depends upon the teacher and the school. As you read this description of Soviet schools, decide how well you would fit as a teacher.

CHAPTER FOCUS

1. Use one or two sentences to express what you think was the central idea of this chapter.

2. Review the list of suggested central ideas. Identify those that are most like yours, and those that are least like yours. What is the reason for the differences?

Suggested Central Ideas

1. The general goal is to teach science processes with specific topics subject to the children's interests and the teacher's previous experience in that area.

2. In the broad framework of the curriculum, the teacher should narrow the experiences to specific objectives based on the children's interest, the teacher's background and ability, and the materials available.

3. "What I should teach?" really asks the question, "Where do I want the learners to go?" If I can define the behavioral outcomes of my learners, then I can more effectively build a learning path.

4. I, the teacher, must decide for each lesson what effect I want to see or find in those children after the lesson is complete.

Based on this decision, I must choose specific topics and activities to bring about the desired effect.

5. In deciding what activities I will use while teaching a science unit, I must keep foremost in my mind the behaviors and understandings I wish the children to attain. Many activities, while related to the topic, may not lead children to the goal of the study.

6. Teachers should teach with a specific objective (child behavior) in mind, utilizing materials, methods, and evaluation to that end.

7. Almost any subject matter can be used by a teacher if he has a definite specific goal in mind or knows what he wants the children to accomplish. In this way, the teacher and the goals are more important than the topic chosen.

8. A teacher should first decide what goals he has for his class. He should then choose from various topics. He might use the ones he feels would be most interesting to the class. He then could choose materials and a method of presentation that would help to reach these objectives.

What Is the Focus
of My Instruction?
Describing Instructional Objectives

Within the long-range goal, there are many specific objectives. A challenging task is to identify those specific objectives which, when combined, will result in the accomplishment of the major goal. If a major goal for science teaching is to teach children to think critically and with an open mind, then the specific objectives of instruction should be like the blocks in a wall—all contributing to the final product.

The analysis of "critical thinking" or "open mindedness" thus becomes a crucial step in achieving this goal. If the child "thinks for himself," what will he do?

Suppose one says that a critical thinker is one who can effectively seek questions and their answers. Since one can obviously seek questions and their answers in history or mathematics, it is relevant to limit the seeking behavior to areas of science. But if the child can seek questions and answers, what will he do? What sub-goals are involved in "seeking questions and their answers"? For example, with a sub-goal of "seeking questions," what further analysis of this goal is possible? If a child seeks questions, what will he do? Must the child generate a question? What observations must he make of the event? What interpretations or extensions beyond his direct observations must he make? What should he do with the situation? What actions are required of him? What past experience or knowledge must he have in order to be able to identify a question about an event? What kind of past experience must he have had to expect to learn from asking a question? What makes him want to ask a question?

Thus, in order for us to analyze the sub-goal of "seeking questions," it is essential that: (1) specific child performance and capabilities are described; (2) specific child characteristics including knowledge level are identified; and (3) the descriptions of the sub-goals are arranged in a sequence that fits the logical and psychological context of both the child and the subject to be learned.

The separation of a long-range goal into its sub-goals and the description of these sub-goals into smaller behaviors of the child must precede instruction. Once the task is completed, it must be continuously revised as new insights about the "question-seeking" behaviors are gained from the use of instructional objectives in planning learning activities.

Thus, in teaching, as in other premeditated activities, knowing where one is going is essential for the planning of how to reach this goal.

Consider the goals of science teaching in these episodes.

Episode 3.1

Miss L. had completed two science studies with her sixth-grade class. The class had been enthusiastically involved in the activities of these studies, and the performance appraisal indicated that they were doing well with observing events, recording, and reporting their observations. Miss L. was becoming concerned, however, as she noted a lack of clarity in the children's interpretations of the results of their investigations. They seemed hesitant to construct more general meanings for specific data. Was this because they needed more experiences in constructing interpretations of data? If so, involving children in a situation where they both collected data and constructed interpretations would be the main goal for the next science study.

From a variety of topics, Miss L. decided she needed a study that would provide a high child-involvement factor, along with the opportunities to make alternative interpretations, both in a context that would stimulate the whole class. A study of magnetic fields seemed a suitable answer. Most of the class had some prior experience with magnets; hence, this would be a start in familiar territory for each child. The study could be structured so that groups of children would collect their own data and make their own interpretations of that data.

Miss L. selected two references on magnetic fields and read more for her own background on the subject.

Before outlining how to initiate the study, she listed results she expected from a study on magnetic fields. At the end of this study, a child should be able to:

1. Construct a chart of the lines of force in a magnetic field.

2. Identify the position of the poles of a magnet, given the lines of force in the magnetic field and the geographical orientation.

3. Construct one or more inferences to explain data shown in his lines of force around the magnets.

4. Describe how data supported an inference about magnetic lines of force.

Miss L. then listed various learning experiences that could be included in a study of magnetic fields.

1. Plot lines of force around a bar magnet using iron filings and wax paper. (She remembered that she would have to help the children as they passed the paper over candles so that the wax would melt and keep the filings positioned.)

2. Iron filings could be used with a glass cover over different magnets. After the children had poured the filings on top of the glass, and gently tapped the glass, they could make drawings of the patterns formed by the filings.

3. Children could construct a compass with a darning needle.

4. Children could also plot the orientation of compass needles as the compass was moved around a bar magnet.

5. A variation of the activity in #4 was for children to tape paper on the floor in different orientations. Using a magnet

and a compass, they could plot the orientation of the compass needle. Then, after the children completed their charts, they displayed them on the wall. Figure out why the charts do not all look the same.

6. Children could suspend a bar magnet from a string and note how it moves.

7. Children could use several charts of compass needle orientations and label the poles of the magnet and tell their reasons for their labels.

8. Some of the able and ambitious children could study the three-dimensional nature of magnetic fields of the earth by embedding a bar magnet in a ball and testing the surface of the ball with a compass needle.

9. Another activity might be to have the children diagram the room locating objects that attract a compass needle: e.g., hidden pipes, metal furniture legs, etc.

Miss L. then examined her list of objectives and suggested activities. She knew the list contained more activities than could be done in the time available for the study—which should she select?

Analysis of Episode 3.1

With the goals or objectives listed on page 28:

1. Which activities would you use?

2. What sequence would you use?

3. What kind of evaluation activities would you use?

Episode 3.2

Mr. C.'s sixth-grade class had just completed a study of sound. He felt the study had been more theoretical than most of his children were ready for at that time. In his search for a new study topic, he reviewed the tentative list he had constructed before school began.

1. Growth and metabulation
2. Forces of moving objects
3. Weather forecasting
4. Magnetic fields
5. Atomic structure of matter

Mr. C. wondered which of these topics might be best. He recalled the fun he had with magnets in the physics lab at the University's summer institute. He thought of many useful activities and started listing them.

1. Children could magnetize a needle and float it on water to determine the North–South line.

2. Children could hang a bar magnet by a thread from a chair and determine which direction was north.

3. Using small compasses, children could plot the orientation of compass needles as the compasses were moved around a bar magnet. (Mr. C. wondered what would happen if he used a circular magnet or a household magnet. Maybe he could interest some group in trying that.)

4. Another activity might be a film on magnetism. (As he listed this, Mr. C. couldn't remember any film in the school catalogue that was on magnets. He did recall hearing Mrs. W. and other sixth-grade teachers say the film they recently used had a good section on lodestones. Maybe that would be a possibility.)

5. Thinking of lodestones, Mr. C. then wondered if a time line of the history of magnets might be a useful activity. He had four or five students in the class who were real history buffs. Where to send them for information was a problem. It's possible that the librarian could help. If that source was inadequate, he could contact the father of Marilyn, a girl in last year's class. Dr. R. was a physicist and very interested in school.

6. Thinking of Marilyn's father made Mr. C. add this item— Have Marilyn's father come and talk to the class. But about

what subject? Mr. C. decided that magnets might be too narrow a topic. He might have Dr. R. describe what a scientist does in order to encourage members of his class to become scientists.

7. After he studied the list, Mr. C. added an item: Have a small number of reports on "What makes a magnet a magnet?"

Mr. C. looked over the list of activities with satisfaction. This study was going to be fun. He began now to organize the study for the class. His first task was to describe the goals for the study. They were:

1. Understand magnetism.
2. Appreciate the beauty of nature's regularity and predictability.
3. Increase the children's ability to think critically.
4. Keep an open mind when drawing conclusions.

Analysis of Episode 3.2

With Mr. C.'s goals or objectives in mind,

1. Which activities would you use?
2. In what sequence would you use the activities?
3. What kind of evaluation activity would you use?

There are some elements common to both Episodes 3.1 and 3.2.

1. Mr. C. and Miss L. both chose a topic.
2. They decided when to begin the topic.
3. They needed to describe how to begin.
4. They needed to decide on when to end the study.
5. They needed to decide on how to end the study.

Decisions on how to begin and when and how to end a study in science are important not only to the teacher, but also to the child. How these two teachers described their goals of instruction made a remarkable difference in the way in which they could make decisions about points 3, 4, and 5.

One way of answering the challenge of structuring child experiences is to examine the statement of instructional goals. If these are stated in terms of what the child should be able to do by the end of instructional experience, there is a far greater probability that relevance and responsibility for learning will exist for the child.

Objectives stated in vague terms, such as: "the child is to gain an understanding," or "to increase his ability to think critically," or "to understand important relations in science," describe important goals. Yet, as stated, these objectives are of questionable value as guides for instruction. They limit the study of science, but they certainly do not provide any direction as to *what* within science one *might expect to see the children doing.*

If objectives are to be useful in structuring experience, they must reflect some specific expected effects of that experience. For example, in the objective, "the child is to gain an understanding of magnetism," what does "understand" mean? Does it mean that the child should be able to use some concept of magnetism in some situation? If so, how and when are these to be used? What specific tasks should the child be able to do? In what specific situation should the child be able to accomplish these tasks? How would the teacher determine whether or not a child has succeeded in accomplishing these specific tasks?

If an objective is to result in child-centered experiences, it must be stated in terms of specific behaviors of the child that can be observed by the teacher. Only then will the objective provide direction for both the learning experience and the appraisal of the effectiveness of that learning experience.

Initial writing of instructional objectives in terms of what the child will be able to do may sometimes be difficult. With experience, this task becomes more manageable. The process follows a simple pattern consisting of three considerations: (1) identification of the behavior desired; (2) description of the situation or the context in which the behavior is to be observed; and (3) description of the extent to which the child should exhibit this behavior. The most effective behavioral objectives are those which reflect all three of these criteria.

Those behaviors which one expects to observe are indicated by verbs denoting action. Teachers cannot observe "knowing" or "understanding" or "appreciating." They can, however, observe a child who is "constructing" or "choosing" or "writing" or "describing." If a child is to be observed, then the teacher must decide where one is to look for that behavior. If a teacher expects children to construct an interpretation, then those situations should be specified in which the children will be constructing the interpretation. For example, will the children be constructing an interpretation of the charts of the magnets or of the magnetic fields or of the orientation of the magnets? It is quite possible that a teacher would consider all of these situations, some of them, or situations which were not mentioned. Unless the situation is identified and described, the objective could lead to many interpretations and, hence, not give specific direction. Statements of objectives assume significance because they allow the teacher to determine the success of the instructional experience.

Instruction can be readily evaluated if the extent of the behavior is defined as a part of each objective. For some objectives, children will or will not be able to perform the task. For many tasks, however, it will be necessary to determine the degree of success. If, for example, the objective were that "the child should describe supporting data for inferences," then the experience will have been successful if the child can accomplish that task and unsuccessful if he cannot. With an objective stated in this manner, there is no measure of partial success. On the other hand, if that same objective were modified to read, "the child will be able to describe at least four kinds of data which support an inference about magnetic lines of force," this situation describes for the teacher the extent of the behavior which a child should display in order for his performance to be accepted as successful.

Properly worded instructional objectives, therefore, include a description of the behavior, description of the situation, and the extent to which the behavior is expected. The situation and extent of the behavior may be implied in the statement of the behavior, but if not clearly implied, they need to be specifically stated.

SUMMARY

Describing instructional objectives is a challenging and rewarding task. The ease with which a teacher can plan a science study and involve children in the activities of that study is totally dependent upon the clarity with which the instructional objectives are defined.

There are three ingredients in a clearly defined and functional objective: First, the instructional objective must have a subject— always the child.

"At the end of this study, the *child* should be able to . . ."

Second, the objective must have a verb that describes observable action rather than abstract verbs such as understanding, discovering, or appreciating. The clearly written objective uses words such as construct, identify, state, or demonstrate.

"At the end of this study, the child should be able to *construct* . . ."

Third, the instructional objective must include a concise description of the action. While it is important for the child to be able to "construct," it is equally important to specify what it is that he should be able to construct.

"At the end of this study, the child should be able to construct *a chart of the lines of force in a magnetic field.*"

Instructional objectives that describe the effects or the behavioral changes expected in children provide a springboard for decisions about instruction—how and when to begin, and how and when to end.

SHARPENING YOUR CONCEPT OF INSTRUCTIONAL OBJECTIVES

The use or misuse of behaviorally stated objectives has been the topic of writing of several thoughtful people. Before you read these selections, you may wish to make a list of the pros and cons that you can think of about the use of performance or behavioral objectives. As you read the articles, add to your list and then draw your own conclusions.

Anderson, Ronald D. "Formulating Objectives for Elementary Science." *Science and Children,* September 1967, pp. 20–23.

Anderson pictures objectives as an essential component of evaluation. He also describes reasons for the desirability of specified objectives. How do you answer Anderson's question, "Can all of our objectives be stated in behavioral terms?"

Atkin, J. Myron. "Behavioral Objectives in Curriculum Design: A Cautionary Note." *The Science Teacher,* May 1968, pp. 27–30.

Atkin describes three specific reservations about behaviorally stated objectives. As you name these reservations, think about how Dr. Atkin would modify Miss L.'s and Mr. C.'s approaches.

Engman, Bill D. "Behavioral Objectives: Keys to Planning." *The Science Teacher,* October 1968, pp. 86–87.

Engman suggests that objectives require careful nurture and proper treatment if they are to mature. In what way does his statement suggest that your concept of objectives might be modified?

Kurtz, Edwin B., Jr. "Help Stamp Out Non-Behavioral Objectives." *The Science Teacher,* January 1965, pp. 31–32.

According to Kurtz, part of the task in translating large desirable goals into specified behaviors is the description of "what it is you want the child to be able to do by the end of the course." He then identifies the result of this approach.

CHAPTER FOCUS

1. State the central idea of Chapter 3.
2. Review the list of suggested central ideas. Identify those which are most like yours, and those that are least like yours. What reasons can you give for the differences?

Suggested Central Ideas

1. Planning curriculum in terms of behavioral objectives focuses the teacher's attention on the children and what they need to know. He then plans activities and experiences which can communicate this knowledge to them. If the objectives are well stated in terms of observable behavior, it will be easy to assess how well the goals are achieved.

2. At the end of every study, the teacher should evaluate the child's learning and his instruction by examining the child's behavioral performance that he formulated at the beginning of the study.

3. Instructional objectives need to be described in concrete terms of observable behavior in children and not in abstract ideas.

4. Instructional objectives are the teacher's means to his end. In other words, by describing clearly any action the child should be able to perform within a given period of time, the teacher is able to clearly determine those tasks and activities which will enable the child to achieve the desired goal, as well as enable the teacher to evaluate the child's success.

5. In designing a teaching situation, the teacher should state his objectives in terms of observable, measurable child behavior, and then analyze the kinds of learning activities which might promote the objectives.

6. Determining the behavioral change that a child will make prior to instruction allows the teacher to organize experiences for the child so that the desired change of behavior occurs during instruction. If no specific behavior is identified, then the organization of experiences is made more difficult, because, while any experience may occur, the teacher and child will not be able to evaluate the experience in terms of learning, but only in terms of vague feelings.

CHAPTER 4

How Do I Involve Children?
Setting the Stage

In a theatrical production, the first impressions both of the stage and of the first scene are those that are etched deepest in one's mind about the play. A drab stage-setting or a dull first scene can be most disappointing. A colorful stage and an "alive" performance can spark one's interest.

Well-designed stage-settings or high-interest first scenes do not just happen. They are a result of both careful planning by the director and skillful development of the abilities of the cast.

In teaching science, the initial experience in a class study may be a dull, uninspiring recital of relevant ideas, or it may be a sparkling, interest-grabbing involvement of the child. In these two episodes, you may wish to contrast the impact of the first experience in a science unit.

Episode 4.1

Mrs. R.'s second-grade class was an alert group of 31 boys and girls. She had found them to be a really "fun" group to work with, and also a challenge. They seemed particularly quick to pick up new ideas and to use them in many situations. She had learned many new concepts from the study on magnets that the children had finished a month before. Mrs. R. knew she should be beginning a new science study and yet she felt hesitant. Suppose the boys and girls knew more than she did about the next study topic —weather. How could she make the study interesting for them?

To teach the concept of water cycles as part of weather, she decided to begin with an illustration of cloud formation and rain —a teakettle experiment.

After school one Monday, Mrs. R. went to the science closet, where she located a piece of glass and a hot plate for the experiment. There wasn't a teakettle in the science closet. That, Mrs. R. decided, she could bring from home. As she walked back to her room with the glass and hot plate, it occurred to her that maybe it would be a good idea for her to check the hot plate to see if it worked properly. In the room, she placed the hot plate on the low demonstration table that was near the chalkboard. Using the only electrical outlet, which was by the table, she plugged in the hot plate and waited. Several minutes later, it still had not started to get warm.

Thinking that Mr. R. might be able to help, she took the hot plate home along with the 31 worksheets of math and language she had to grade that evening.

Mr. R. replaced the plug on the hot plate cord, and it worked satisfactorily. He asked his wife what she was going to do with the hot plate. She said that it would help her start a study on weather because it was an experiment which showed why it rained.

At the regular science time the next day, Mrs. R. had the children clear their desks and get ready for science. The boys and girls quickly followed her directions. On the bulletin board, Mrs. R. had placed a picture of the water cycle but without labels.

She introduced the unit by suggesting that today they would name the parts of the water cycle on the bulletin board. To help them in selecting names for the parts of the water cycle, the children should observe what would happen. Mrs. R. sat down beside the demonstration table and turned on the hot plate. On the hot plate, she placed her teakettle, which contained a small amount of water. (She had found out that if you fill the teakettle too full, it takes quite a long time for it to boil and the children become restless.) Near the opening in the teakettle, she held the piece of glass. In about two minutes, steam began to rise and moisture began to fog the glass. Several boys and girls said they saw white stuff come out of the kettle and they saw water run down the glass. They wondered where the white stuff had come from. In answer to

Mrs. R.'s question about what the white stuff was, the class agreed that it was steam. Mrs. R. then pointed out that water was in the kettle; as the water was heated it turned to steam; the steam came out of the kettle and hit the glass; there it collected ("You call this condensation," and she wrote the word on the board); when enough steam had collected, it began to run off, like rain.

The lesson was moving along well, Mrs. R. thought. She moved to the bulletin board. She pointed out that, in the experiment, they started out with water in the kettle. The children then identified water in the pond as similar. They also labeled the cloud as being like steam and the rain as being like water running down the glass.

To summarize the first experiment, Mrs. R. then pointed out that the water cycle helps us to explain why it rains.

Just then, a thunderstorm developed outside. There was a loud clap of thunder and lightning, followed by a terrific downpour. James, who had been quietly listening, looked out the window and then walked over to Mrs. R. and said, "But Mrs. R., where is the teakettle?"

Analysis of Episode 4.1

If you were Mrs. R., how would you have answered James?

What interest-grabbing event did Mrs. R. use?

At the end of the first activities, what did Mrs. R. know about how easily the children could achieve the expected results of this unit on weather?

Episode 4.2

Mrs. F. had been looking forward to this year's second-grade class. Two of the first-grade teachers who had taught several of the boys and girls assigned to her class told Mrs. F. what a challenge these children had been. They were bundles of energy, and there was a real concern in her mind of how to direct that energy.

Then Mrs. F. had become ill and surgery had kept her out of school until the early part of November. When she returned, she found that the substitute teachers had done their best, but there was much work to be done to catch up. It was not until after the Thanksgiving holidays that she was able to introduce their first science study.

In the southern city where they lived, changes in weather became more obvious in November than in September. Because Mrs. F. wanted to watch and listen for the kinds of observations her children would make, she chose to do a study on weather. To her, weather provided an excellent situation in which children needed to make more than a single observation in order to adequately describe an event. In her plans, Mrs. F. had listed her objectives as:

At the end of this study, the children should be able to:

1. Record weather conditions on a chart using standard symbols and read these recorded symbols.
2. Distinguish between weather conditions of two days by examining the weather chart.

On the Monday after the Thanksgiving holiday, Mrs. F. was ready with several possible introductions. The class could discuss precipitation or clouds or wind or temperature. Monday morning showed her the first step. During the night, a "blue norther" had blown in. Temperatures had plunged from the high eighties to the mid-fifties.

After a sharing time with the holiday experiences, Mrs. F. quieted the discussion and looked slowly about the room. Aloud, she wondered in what way the room was different today from the way it had been last Wednesday, before the vacation.

Several answers were volunteered. The floor had been waxed. (Indeed it had. Mrs. F. hadn't noticed that!) The bulletin board had been changed in that the turkey was gone and a large chart had been placed there. (Mrs. F. was pleased that someone had noticed. Maybe the supervisor would notice also!) The desks were arranged in a U shape rather than in rows. Different children had on different colored dresses and shirts.

After a few minutes, Mrs. F. hinted that there was something or a group of somethings in the room that had not been there last Wednesday. Puzzled eyes searched the room. The children did not recall that last Wednesday had been a very warm day while today was so cool that everyone had worn a coat, and the coak rack on the wall of the room was filled. When Mrs. F. asked if the coat rack were any different today, children quickly responded that, yes, they had worn coats today but had not last Wednesday.

Mrs. F. then wondered aloud as to why they had worn coats. Because it was cold, the class answered and shivered with delight. "How can you tell if it's colder today?" Mrs. F. asked.

One boy suggested that you looked to see if the wind was blowing. Several agreed with him. One other child, however, countered that every time the wind blows it's not cold. That seemed to be a good puzzler and the group did not seem ready to resolve it.

Another child suggested that you used one of "those things that go up and down." Several thought this was also a good idea. Mrs. F. probed a little further by asking the girl to tell more about "those things that go up and down." The girl explained that she didn't remember its name but when it got warm the red line would move. Another child said he thought the thing was called a thermometer. Several others agreed that that was the correct name.

Mrs. F. was still probing to find out what the children knew about thermometers. She asked another how he could tell it was colder by looking at the thermometer. He quickly replied with confidence that if the red line went up, it was colder. Mrs. F. paused a moment. ("If it goes up, it is colder"—did he really mean that?) She asked George's neighbor to tell her what George had said. The boy repeated George's statement and said that's what he thought, too. Now it was Mrs. F.'s turn to be puzzled. She checked around the room. Thirty-five of the thirty-six members of her class all agreed that when it got colder, the red line on a thermometer went up! One boy, Bill, disagreed.

Mrs. F. asked Bill why he didn't agree with everyone else. He quickly replied that he had watched the red line of a thermometer when he had put it in a glass of ice water. He knew that the red line of the thermometer went down—not up—when it got cold.

It was time to go to music, but Mrs. F. smiled with satisfaction. She had set the stage and her task was defined.

Analysis of Episode 4.2

If you were Mrs. F., what would you do in the next science period?

What interest-grabbing event did Mrs. F. use?

At the end of the first activity, what did Mrs. F. know about the children's ability to achieve the expected results of the study of weather?

An analogy was introduced at the beginning of this topic in which the teacher is implied to be somewhat like the director of a theatrical production. Although both the teacher and the director are responsible for a number of tasks, such as setting the stage, guiding, and appraising, the task of setting the stage has a high priority for the teacher.

Stage-setting is a way of describing the initial structuring of a learning experience, and it is a task of no small magnitude. This pre-planning and initial activity includes the securing of desirable student materials, and arranging them for convenience and accessibility. Much lost motion comes from bottlenecks in the arrangement of the classroom. For example, if there is only one focus of attention in the classroom, are children arranged so that all will have a front-row seat? Or are they arranged so that only five can see and so that it takes six times the effort for other children to observe an event? Thinking ahead and anticipating children's responses can add desirable dimensions to the learning experience.

While setting a stage, the director is not only concerned with the props on the floor, but also directs great attention to the background which communicates a tone or an atmosphere to the star's performance.

What is the tone of your classroom? Does its dreariness speak of your weariness? Does its dramatic flash of color reflect your sparkle and interest? Do your displays end with question marks or exclamation points? Your classroom reflects much of yourself. If one is the giver of information, one may tend to have displays of that information in the room. If one is a director of thinking, however, one uses displays that cause children to "observe and ponder," rather·than merely to "look and see."

Diagnosing performance is the second phase of setting the stage. A director recognizes that each star in a theatrical production is an individual capable of discovering for himself the enjoyment of success. He carefully listens to the rehearsal, which is the first experience. He observes mannerisms, voice inflections, superficial role interpretations, and other key behaviors. The director then selects the appropriate means to help each player improve his performance. He recognizes that "telling" the actor his gesture was inappropriate will not help the actor. Rather, the director, with the performer, usually explores and practices better ways in which to move the hand.

Teachers have a similar role. To identify those areas in which children need help, one should start with a situation in which the child must attempt to perform those behaviors described as objectives. The teacher watches, listens, and observes a variety of activities, and then selects those experiences which each child needs.

The child's problem may be use of a poor inference or an inability to express himself or a lack of skill in manipulating an apparatus. Obviously, not all children will have the *same* need. But all children will have *some* needs. Use of the initial learning situation to assist in diagnosing those needs is a key to successful teaching. In diagnosing the performance, not only is the teacher given the opportunity to identify what it is the child cannot do, but the child can see just what it is he *needs* to learn. This first experience can then be a tremendous boost to establishing readiness in the child for what is to come next. The teacher must keep an open mind here, however. If the child demonstrates his ability to perform the objective during the pre-test, then the teacher must accept this performance and be ready to move on to a new set of behaviors. Teaching the child to do what he can do already is a task that invites frustration for the teacher, boredom for the child, and discipline disasters for the entire class.

There are several specific strategies you may find useful in setting the stage.

First, initiate a new setting by displaying those objects you intend to use and then let the children decide for themselves what they can do with these objects, rather than telling the children what everybody is going to do and why. This procedure provides time for the children to explore the material, and allows the teacher an opportunity to listen carefully to the ideas which the children express.

Second, when a child makes a specific suggestion as to what he can do with the material, encourage him to try out his suggestion rather than discuss its merits with him before he has an opportunity to find this out for himself. Observing him in the process of discovery will tell you far more than forcing his agreement. (He really has little choice much of the time.)

Third, keep an open mind as to what children suggest rather than insisting that they accept the answer that you provide. In a learning situation, boys and girls are quick to perceive whether you really want their ideas or whether you are seeking a single "correct" answer. In the stage-setting phase, you should be concerned with securing as many ideas as possible rather than a single correct one.

Fourth, set up the introductory experience so that children are actively involved either physically or mentally, rather than watching you do the action yourself. It makes little difference in a good diagnosis for a physician to know his own blood count. He needs to know the blood count of his patient. While it is important to be able to balance a scale, measure a table, or know that the red line in a thermometer goes up when it gets warmer, it is much more important to have the children do these tasks themselves and for you to find out what they can learn from those tasks.

Fifth, base your opinions on what you *see* the children do rather than on what you *assume* they can do. If Mrs. F. (in Episode 4.2) had assumed that the children could use a thermometer, it is obvious that she would soon encounter difficulties. It is thus highly important in setting the stage that you provide opportunities for the children to display their behavior or the lack of the behavior which is described in your set of expected results.

SUMMARY

The best learning situations usually occur where there is an appropriate mixture of child and teacher. The child is the star. The action and the spotlight are focused on him. As a star of the production, the child must have a stage upon which to operate. Selecting this stage, setting it up with desirable materials, and making sure it fits the children's needs are significant tasks for the teacher.

Getting started with the production may represent a point at which children will need assistance. Because the director of a theatrical production recognizes that each star is an individual capable of rich and meaningful experiences, he listens carefully during the initial activities. The director selects the appropriate means to help the star improve his performance.

Similarly, the child is observed by the teacher–director. Those areas in which the child needs assistance are identified by creating a situation in which the child must perform the specific behaviors described as expected results of the study. Through watching and listening the experiences needed by each child are determined. The learning situation is a tool for diagnosing the relevance of experience and the ability each child has to accept his responsibility in the new learning situation.

SHARPENING YOUR STAGE-SETTING BEHAVIOR

Setting the stage for instruction includes your behavior as a teacher. The stage itself may limit, to some extent, the flexibility that is possible.

Gardner, Robert. "How Much Does Air Weigh?" *Science and Children*, May 1968, pp. 14–15.

Gardner describes another strategy in setting the stage—an interest-grabbing student starting point. You will find it interesting to read what he used and what he learned in the first stage-setting experience he used during his instruction.

Labahn, William F. "So You Want to Provide a Modern Science Program." *School Science and Math,* November 1969, pp. 695–99.

Based on pre-selection of goals, Labahn describes some concerns related to setting the stage for instruction. With reference to the organizational pattern of the school, Labahn believes that a flexible room, materials, and schedule are essentials for science instruction.

Melby, Mabel O. *et al.* "Fostering Individualization in the Classroom." In Doll, R. C., ed., *Individualizing Instruction.* (Washington, D.C.: Association for Supervision and Curriculum Development, 1964), pp. 75–85.

The role of the teacher in guiding requires the teacher to be alert to the child. Melby emphasizes that teachers respond to some clues while ignoring others. Time and timing are key ideas in guiding children.

Miel, Alice. "Organization Doesn't Make the Difference." *The Instructor,* October 1968, pp. 31, 116.

Miel discusses one aspect of setting the stage—namely, the organizational setting for teaching. She contrasts a self-contained classroom with an integrated, non-graded grouping as an organizational stage for science instruction.

Verduin, John R., Jr. "Implementing the Scientific Method in the Elementary School." *Science Education,* March 1968, pp. 162–67.

Verduin describes stage-setting for a situation involving fifth-grade children which includes a pre-appraisal activity. He illustrates the desirability of the child's seeing evidence that the stage-setting and pre-appraisal are related to an instructional goal. Verduin also suggests possibilities related to the role of the teacher who doesn't know the answer to a problem.

CHAPTER FOCUS

1. Use one or two sentences to express what you think is the central idea of Chapter 4.

2. Review the list of suggested central ideas. Identify those that are most like yours, and those that are least like yours. What do you suggest is the reason for these differences?

Suggested Central Ideas

1. A teacher should give each science study an interesting introduction which will help draw the children into revealing what they already know and what they want to know about the topic.

2. Beginning a lesson is a most crucial process in teaching, and a teacher can often arouse the greatest curiosity and interest in youngsters by beginning with something they have recently experienced.

3. Stage-setting involves two things: (a) pre-planning, which includes securing materials, arranging these and the class, anticipating child responses, and creating a learning "tone" in the classroom, and (b) diagnosing a situation in which the child attempts to perform those behaviors described as objectives.

4. In setting the stage for learning, the teacher must determine what previous experience the class has had (learned by listening and observing), and, based upon this, decide how to structure the new learning experience to meet the needs of the class.

5. In beginning a lesson, the teacher should involve the children mentally and/or physically in an atmosphere in which the *child* is taking the responsibility for his actions. This experience should do two things: (a) allow the teacher to know where the child is in relation to the objectives, and (b) arouse in the child an interest in the experiences which may follow.

6. It is the teacher's responsibility to create an interest and to motivate the children to want to learn.

CHAPTER 5

How Do I Keep Children Involved?

Guiding the Star

or the Student

The word *educate* is itself a clue to the intended function of schools and teaching. In its Latin origin, it means literally "to lead out of." Once it is clear where the child is to go—when expected results are defined and the child has demonstrated his ability or lack of ability to perform the expected behaviors—the situation is open to guidance. Guidance is the direction of a learning process determined by skillfully probing and using the children's responses in the construction of new experiences.

How does one guide a child? What are the alternate ways to teach children? In the learning episodes which follow, you may find it useful to identify those behaviors of the teacher which are examples of situations in which children were being guided toward learning objectives.

Episode 5.1

A group of fourth-grade boys and girls had been measuring the time a candle would burn under various glass jars. Their data indicated that if a single jar and candles of like size were used and the burning time measured, the results were 14, 13, 18, 12, and 16 seconds. The group decided that 15 seconds would be the best estimate for the burning time for the candle in Jar B. They later discovered it was a quart jar. In a similar way, they determined the burning time for Jar A (a pint jar) and Jar C (a half-pint jar). Mrs. O. helped the children summarize their results by recording them on the chalkboard.

JAR	AVERAGE BURNING TIME IN SECONDS
A	15
B	8
C	5

One of the expected results of this study on candle-burning time was that the children would be able to construct predictions from graphs. Mrs. O. recalled discussions with two of the third-grade teachers who had previously taught her students. She was concerned about what skills the children had learned in constructing graphs. The two teachers warned Mrs. O. that they had not taught graphing skills in third grade and they felt very sure that the children did not know how to construct a graph. Since constructing a graph was essential to the success of the study, and since the children probably did not know how to do this, what should Mrs. O. do? She pondered the alternatives. She could just ask the children to construct a graph of the data and then observe how well they would do. She could graph the candle-burning-time data while the children watched, and explain to them the parts of the graph and how to use it. She could use a new set of transparencies on graphing which illustrated the parts of the graph with cartoon figures.

Mrs. O. selected the first alternative because she felt it most important to identify what the children could do *before* deciding what kind of guiding activities would be appropriate.

The next day, Mrs. O. gave each of the children a blank piece of paper. They reviewed the data on candle-burning time. Mrs. O. asked the children what other ways they could use to keep records of the results. Pictures were suggested; paragraph reports were mentioned. Mrs. O. noticed that no one mentioned making a graph. She then posed this task for the children: "Make a graph of your data."

Puzzled foreheads quickly confirmed what Mrs. O. had suspected—most of the class was genuinely confused. Two or three children began to draw grids but seemed unable to do more than that. Two boys, however, were hard at work. This interested Mrs. O. and she walked to their desks to observe and listen. Both boys were busy drawing giraffes.

Obviously Mrs. O. had diagnosed a need in her children. They did not know how to construct a graph.

Since a graph is a pictorial way of recording information, Mrs. O. decided to introduce the idea to her children by having them record some specific information. She had the children form five groups.

The task for the children was for them to make a picture of how they were arranged in the room. Their pictures were to show who was seated where. Each of the groups set about doing the task. Some drew diagrams of the room which included many relevant points of reference such as the windows and doorways that identified the location of each team. Most of the illustrations represented each child in the group by drawing stick figures near a desk.

Mrs. O. observed the progress of the class and listened to the children's comments. She then posed a second task. Suppose she wanted to compare Team A with Team C—what kinds of comparisons might she make? A quick response was that Team C had one more child than Team A. Mrs. O. continued to have the boys and girls describe comparisons of numbers of children in each team. She then gave each child a colored cube. In response to the question, how could they use the cube to show how many children were in Team A, the children suggested that they could stack the cubes.

One boy then added, "By each group making a stack, you could compare the number of members in each group." The others followed his suggestion and soon they had an arrangement of cubes.

It was then time for the class to go to the library. Mrs. O. had the cube groups placed on her desk and the children left for the next activity. When they returned to the classroom, the children found the desks rearranged into a large U-shape. Mrs. O. returned to the groups of cubes on her desk. She asked several children to describe for her the story these cubes were telling. With some hesitancy and after several partial successes, the children concluded that each cube group represented how many boys and girls were on each team. They also described the convenience of labeling the stacks so that they would know which group of cubes represented which team of children.

Mrs. O. then turned to a grid on the chalkboard. She posed the task: "Suppose I wanted to keep a record of our grouping this morning. How could I use this chart?" The class quickly suggested that she could color in blocks on the chart. Mrs. O. handed chalk to one girl and asked her to show what the class meant. With the help of a second girl, she filled in the blocks with five colors.

Mrs. O. pointed to the second column and asked Boyd what information he could tell her about it. When he replied that it told him that there were five children on Team B, Mrs. O. wondered how he knew that. She could not see any five children on that chart. Several boys and girls suggested that Boyd was right, but that the chart needed some labels, just like the piles of cubes needed names. They labeled the base line "Groups" and the left side "Number of Children." Using several questions, such as "Which team had the same numbers as Team C?" and "Which team had one more member than Team A?" and "Which team had less than Team D?" Mrs. O. observed that most of the class was able to use the graph to describe the number of children in the groups.

She turned to the data on candle-burning time. The next task for the children was to describe in what way they could use a graph to record their results. It was obvious that this seemed to be a large step in thinking for many of the children. With the large chart on the chalkboard, one child suggested that they could put the number of seconds on the left side, since it already had numbers on it. Another child asked how, when there were only ten lines in the number of seconds. His neighbor responded that they could count by twos or by fives. The class agreed to label the left side by counting by twos and to label the bottom of the graph with the jars.

Mrs. O. gave each pair of children a sheet of graph paper and asked them to make a graph using the data on the candle-burning time. As they worked, she again observed and listened. When a child seemed puzzled, she was there to help with a question to re-direct his thinking or action. Mrs. O. was pleased with the prog-ress of the children. She found that when they were given hypo-thetical jars and burning times, the boys and girls were quickly able to point out the appropriate point on the graph for recording the data.

She was now ready to continue the study, using the graphs to construct predictions.

Analysis of Episode 5.1

Mrs. O. diagnosed the children's inability to construct a graph. By the end of the activity, they could accomplish the task. Name three teaching strategies she used in guiding the children.

Describe one alternative Mrs. O. could have used to teach the children how to construct a graph.

Episode 5.2

Mrs. V.'s class of first-graders was a lively group. They lived with great zest and enjoyment. She gained much satisfaction from watching these six-year-olds meet new experiences with refreshing curiosity. For her next science study, Mrs. V. was going to use an-imals to help the children improve their skill in description. New experiences are fun, but they become more meaningful when one can share those experiences with others. In two earlier studies, the children had been working with concepts of two- and three-dimen-sional shapes and of symmetry. They had done quite well. The new study would be useful as an exercise in which the children could learn to describe animals using two- and three-dimensional shapes, and also applying their knowledge of the concept of sym-metry.

To begin the study, Mrs. V. gave each child a piece of construction paper shaped either as a triangle, a rectangle, a square, a circle, or an ellipse. She held up a shape like a circle and asked how many had a shape like hers. Several raised their hands. She also identified it as "like a circle." She then held up a shape like a triangle. Those that had this shape also held theirs up. She asked Ken what was the name of the shape like the one she held in her hand. He replied "rectangle." Not knowing if he had mixed the two words that sound alike—triangle and rectangle—or if he really wasn't able to distinguish between a triangle and a rectangle, she then asked him, "How many sides does your shape have?" He replied, "Two." Mrs. V. was puzzled. She then asked Ken to show what he meant. Ken quickly pointed to the front and the back of the paper shape. Then Mrs. V. saw what he meant. She rephrased her question. "How many edges does your shape have?" He quickly replied that it had three edges. Mrs. V. then held up a shape like a rectangle. "How many edges does this have?" Ken counted four edges.

Mrs. V. continued, asking Ken in what way were the two shapes different. He said one had three edges and the other had four edges. He went on to identify those shapes that have three edges as triangles and those that had four edges as rectangles.

Mrs. V. then asked Ken to find a shape like a triangle on an animal picture. He pointed to the back of the goose and to the horn of the cow.

Satisfied with Ken's response, Mrs. V. was ready to continue the lesson.

Analysis of Episode 5.2

Suppose Mrs. V. had responded to Ken's description of the triangular sheet as having two sides by saying, "No, Ken, it really has three sides, don't you see?" What do you think Ken would have said or done during the rest of the lesson?

Describe two things Mrs. V. did to help guide Ken's behavior.

Describe one alternative way in which she could have responded to Ken.

In these learning episodes, the teachers were leading children out of confusion and into clarity and accuracy. Both teachers knew where they were going. Both teachers also knew that it was most important that the child be able to perform the task—that the child be the star, not the teacher.

To guide her "star" without up-staging or dominating the scene required careful planning by the teacher. In both situations, the teacher:

1. Secured a response from the class (construct a graph or identify a shape).

2. Structured a new situation (record groups or count the edges) based on the first response.

3. Secured new responses in which the children used the new behavior (graph candle data, find shape like a triangle in the goose and the cow).

A key to guiding children is to realize that to gain a new behavior requires many experiences in many new situations. Each of us learns a new idea or acquires a new behavior when he has an opportunity to (1) discriminate—to look at things that belong, and at things that don't belong, to an idea; (2) describe—tell how those things that belong to an idea are alike. This task is really the description of essential parts of the idea (for example, a triangle has three edges); and (3) the application of the idea or behavior to a new situation.

With these basic, general ideas to guide children, here are some specific strategies you may find useful:

First, once you have immersed a group of children in a situation, provide them with time to grope, ponder, and "mess around" with the objects and events that make up that situation. *You* may know quite well what skill or concept lies within the experience. *You* may see quite clearly which observations will support the idea. But the child will need time to manipulate the experience from *his* frame of reference and interest. He will not be ready for an analysis of "how it fits together" until he first has completed some "fitting together" tasks. By having him describe both what he observes and what he still wants to observe, you can help sharpen his observations by pinpointing vague statements and unfounded generalizations.

A second strategy is to develop the skill of listening to a child's description of his experience. Embedded in these descriptions will be a wealth of information for you. Rather than accepting the first response, you can often be most helpful to a child by pushing him to be more precise. "Tell me more about it." "How much bigger?" Probing the basis of a description will enable you to assist the child in separating observed evidence from inference or embroidery of facts!

A third strategy is to develop an awareness of the type of questions you use. Are they structured to make a child think or to force him to give the response you think is correct? The contrast in the responses to these two questions is obvious: "For what reasons did the plants change?" "The plants wilted because they had no water, didn't they?" The productivity of questions is limited by how you structure them. Asking questions to secure a "yes" or "no" reply generally gives little information about the child's performance ability: "Can you make a graph?" On the other hand, if you really want to know if he can make a graph, a rephrased question will secure the information: "Please make a graph of this data."

A fourth strategy involves the illustration of an idea in use. You should select illustrations of an idea that are progressively less obvious than the simpler ones you start with. Just because a child distinguishes an inference from a prediction in a simple situation does not mean that he can distinguish these statements in all situations. When you think the child has acquired an idea, continue to guide him by providing new situations in which he can apply those ideas. One way in which to do this is to introduce a situation that doesn't fit or that may be a surprise fit. As the child identifies how the situation fits or doesn't fit, he will be changing his mental concepts rather than relying on you to tell him he is wrong or that he doesn't see the point.

A fifth strategy employs timing. Involve the children in the experience before you expect analysis and meaning for the labels of that experience (vocabulary words). Naming an experience *after* one has had first-hand familiarity with the experience is the most important strategy.

A sixth strategy concerns involving children as an activity proceeds. Many situations may not lend themselves to each child having a set of equipment. You can have each child involved by providing time for him to express an opinion before actually doing the activity. In this way, rather than the activity being a demonstration—monologue between you and one or two children, all the children are actively involved in comparing actual results with their own expectations.

SUMMARY

In a learning situation, the child is the star. When a teacher identifies an area in which his "performance" needs assistance, that teacher becomes a guide.

A director of a theatrical production recognizes that telling the star that his foot stomp or hand gesture is not adequate will not, of itself, correct the flaw. Rather, he must stand beside the star and, as the star's partner, show him how to perform the task.

When guiding children, a teacher also finds a "telling" approach limited. The telling approach to teaching began in the Medieval Ages when there were no sources of information other than the teacher. Today there are many sources for a child's experiences. These range from the aquarium in the first-grade classroom to electrical apparatus. Involving the child in these resources so that he becomes the star performer is a real challenge. This challenge can result in rewarding success if the child's responses are handled in such a way that he gains a new respect for his own ability to deal with the situation. Within the context provided by the skillful teacher—director, the child initiates action and accepts responsibility for those actions. The child explores his environment; he handles and manipulates it. He also explores the largely untried realm of thinking by relating events of his experience, developing and testing ideas about these events. Learning about his environment and his thinking are extended as the child organizes himself to explore. This he accomplishes by evaluating his own deductions, by making mistakes, by refining his approach to the search for understanding. In this way, the child's role is one of learning to manipulate and control his environment through guided exploration.

Guiding in this way could be described simply as the child learning to do by doing. But this is not quite complete. The child learns to do under the guidance and direction of the teacher. The teacher is the one who structures the learning situation, the one who carefully watches and listens to the learning activities, the one who stimulates and encourages the learner, and the one who provides the background of direction for the learner through skillful questioning and challenging.

SHARPENING YOUR DEFINITION OF GUIDING STUDENTS

Melby and Williams discuss the relationship between self-acceptance, confidence, and creative solutions to old concerns. Glass bases his discussion on the processes of science as a social undertaking. Before reading these selections, you might find it useful to list ways in which a teacher, through guiding, can help a child *know himself better.* Modify your list as you read these selections.

Glass, H. Bentley. "The Most Critical Aspect of Science Teaching." *The Science Teacher,* May 1967, pp. 19–23.

One function of science teaching is expressed in the statement, "Seeing is believing." Glass describes the second function of the laboratory experience as "to learn how to investigate quite a variety of scientific problems." He provides incidents that illustrate this role in guiding science learning experiences.

Melby, Mabel O. *et al.* "Providing Opportunities for Individual Learners to Reveal Themselves." In Doll, R. C., ed., *Individualizing Instruction.* (Washington, D.C.: Association for Supervision and Curriculum Development, 1964), pp. 85–97.

In guiding the children, Melby indicates that acceptance is a goal. The image of the teacher as a real—or unreal—person is reflected in the range of responses. After watching teachers guide children in learning episodes, identify situations in which the teachers demonstrated that they were real or that the children's responses (although incorrect or unexpected) were acceptable. The author relates discovery to the establishment of expectations of ourselves as individuals—a point that is relevant in science instruction.

Williams, Frank E. "Intellectual Creativity and the Teacher." *The Journal of Creative Behavior*, Spring 1967, pp. 173–80.

According to Williams, creativity is dependent upon large amounts of information and upon our willingness and opportunities to use that information. This has implications for science teaching, he says.

CHAPTER FOCUS

1. Use one or two sentences to express what you think is the central idea of this chapter.

2. Review the list of suggested central ideas. Identify those that you think are most like yours and those that are least like yours. What is the difference?

Suggested Central Ideas

1. The teacher must allow children to manipulate the objects of their experiments themselves. But the teacher must be alert to structure experiences which don't fit into the child's ideas or which don't use the child's past experiences to explore new experiences.

2. The teacher must be aware of her methods of guiding children in their search for understanding so that she leads them to seek and find answers rather than merely telling them the answers to questions they have not posed.

3. In "guiding the star," the teacher structures a situation in which the child can learn (and move toward the expected behavioral goal), by asking questions and by presenting new situations

in which the newly learned experience can be used to stimulate better understanding.

4. Teaching should be the leading of youngsters through structured experiences so that the youngsters can evaluate, explain, and describe their experiences to others while expanding their own abilities and intelligence.

5. The method of teaching should result in the child's gaining respect for his ability to deal with the situation—he explores; he initiates action; he manipulates his environment.

6. Strategies for "guiding the star" require the instructor to analyze and "direct" the learner in many unique ways, involving the learner with his environment, his past experiences, his powers of reasoning, and his skills or processes.

7. The teacher teaches by guiding the children to learn by manipulating their own thoughts and experiences for themselves.

CHAPTER 6

How Do I Know When
to Stop?
Assessing Progress

A chess player determines each move on the basis of a master game plan, subject to where on the board he is at the moment. Similarly, a science teacher conducts a study unit on the basis of clearly defined objectives, subject to the present status of the children in the learning process. To determine the class's current status in relation to a master plan requires an appraisal of the results of one's teaching compared with the stated objectives of the study. To make such an appraisal, one must place the child in a situation in which he demonstrates what he can do. The teacher can then compare expected results with actual performance, and consequently decide what new experience will best contribute to the child's learning.

Just as the director decides what to do next by reading the first night's reviews in the newspaper, you as the teacher decide what needs to be done by reading your children's behavior. Designing situations in which you can observe the child's behavior as it is described in your objective is the secret of effective appraising and re-diagnosis.

What kinds of appraisal activities can be used? How can one be sure that an appraisal activity is a true picture of what the child can do? In these episodes, you may wish to identify the goals of the science instruction and the appraisal activities applied to each goal.

Episode 6.1

In Mrs. F.'s kindergarten class, the children had been studying animals. She had a wide variety of animals in the classroom. There was a hamster, a duck, an earthworm, a parakeet, a turtle, a goldfish, a snail, and a kitten.

For three weeks, Mrs. F.'s class had been observing the animals: what they ate, their behavior, even their odors. Mrs. F.'s goals for this study were for the children to be able to:

1. Identify observable characteristics of the animals.

2. Group the animals based on those observable characteristics.

Near the end of the third week, Mrs. F. gathered the boys and girls in a large circle on the rug for study time. She showed them a selection of pictures—one for each animal they had in the room —and asked the children to tell her about the pictures. The boys and girls began to name several things they had observed about each animal. Suzanne suddenly became excited, "Mrs. F., you've got a picture for each animal we have in the room." The others agreed, except Tom. He pointed to the picture of the duck and then to an empty pan and said the duck wasn't there. Mrs. F. smiled; they had taken the duck home two days before—the smell and the noise was a bit too much! The group of children agreed, however, that the pictures were of animals like those in the room, at least at one time.

Mrs. F. then asked how they might organize or group the pictures. John wanted to be first. He picked out pictures of the hamster, the turtle, and the parakeet and put them together. Mrs. F. and several others in the class wondered why they belonged together. John replied, "Because they all have toe nails!" Dave then suggested that ducks also belonged in this group, for they had toe nails too.

The next day, Mrs. F. settled the class near the board where she had placed John and David's group. She asked if they could make some other groups. After many ideas were tried out, the class finally agreed upon the following:

| Hamster | Duck | Snail | Fish |
| Kitten | Parakeet | | Turtle |

They agreed as to the reasons—fur, feathers, shell, and live in water. Mrs. F. wondered what to do with the earthworm. The class decided that they needed to have another group—those that live in the ground.

Analysis of Episode 6.1

What were the goals for Mrs. F.'s science study?

What appraisal activity did she have for each goal?

Episode 6.2

Mr. G. had completed a study on measuring in his fourth-grade class. The children had experienced some difficulty with learning the ideas of area measurement and the relationship between various units of linear measuring. Because he sensed the restlessness of the children, due to the length of time spent on the study, Mr. G. announced a final test for the measurement unit before they would begin a study of rocks. The test he gave the children included these items:

1. Here is a field belonging to Farmer Smith.

Give the formula for finding the area of the field.

2. Farmer Smith also has a silo next to his barn.

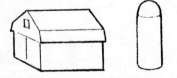

Give the formula for finding the volume of his silo.

3. Fill in the blanks:

_____ inches = 1 foot

One mile = _____ feet

_____ inches = 1 yard

_____ feet = 1 yard

_____ square inches = 1 square foot

_____ square feet = 1 square yard

Analysis of Episode 6.2

List the behaviors which Mr. G.'s test measured.

List Mr. G.'s goals.

In what way are the goals reflected in the test?

Episode 6.3

Another teacher in the same school with Mr. G., Mrs. C., had also finished a study of measuring. It had gone quite well for her class. She had been directing her children toward being able to state the method to be used in measuring a situation, and to state the rule that was the basis for its use. In the science study, they had used animal footprints as a means of studying area, and inflated balloons in studying volume.

To appraise the children's progress, Mrs. C. gave them these tasks:

1. Here's a diagram of a farmer's field. He wants to cover the field with fertilizer.

What measurements should he make of this field?

2. If he knew that a bag of fertilizer would cover one square meter of land, how many bags of fertilizer would he need if the field were 20 meters × 10 meters?

3. Show how you found your answer.

4. What rule did you use?

5. The same farmer had a corn crib in which to store corn. He wants to know how much corn he can put in that crib. What measurement would he need to make of the crib?

6. If he knew that one bushel of corn filled one square meter of space, how many bushels would the crib hold if it were 10 x 10 x 20 meters?

7. Show how you found your answer.

8. Which rule did you use?

Analysis of Episode 6.3

List the behaviors Mrs. C.'s test measured.

List Mrs. C.'s goals.

In what way do the goals compare with the test?

What information did each teacher gain that would assist him in deciding what needed to be done next with measuring?

Episode 6.4

Miss M. and Mrs. S. had been cooperating quite closely in studies of plants in their sixth-grade classrooms. The studies had captured a new high of student interest. With many plants, the two classrooms had been directed toward objectives that Miss M. and Mrs. S. had identified. At the end of this study, the children were to be able to:

1. State a testable hypothesis for a given situation.

2. Construct a test for the hypothesis.

When both classes came to the end of the science study, the teachers gave an evaluation experience (the children called it a test). Mrs. S.'s test looked like this:

Unit Quiz

1. What are the two chief functions of the stems of plants?

2. What are two kinds of work done by roots of plants?

3. What is the chief work of the flower?

4. What is the chief work of leaves?

5. What two kinds of work are done by seeds?

6. What part of a plant is always present when it is making food?

7. What gas is taken in from the air and used by plants in making food?

8. What waste gas do plants give off?

9. Why do plants set far from a window shed leaves and grow long stems?

10. What is the most important difference between ferns and other types of house plants?

Fill in the Blanks

Ferns

Capillary

Pistil

Fertilizer

Pollen

Root Hairs

Cutting

Bulb

Stems

1. _____ grow on larger roots and take in water for the plant.

2. _____ are plants which never produce flowers or seeds.

3. _____ of plants grow so that they hold the leaves to the light.

4. _____ is a material which is added to the soil to provide plants with needed minerals.

5. _____ action results when water passes upward in small spaces in soil.

6. A_____ is made up of a bud and thick leaves containing stored food.

Miss M.'s test was like this:

1. State a hypothesis.

2. Describe how you would test it.

Analysis of Episode 6.4

What evidence did each teacher have that the children had achieved the objectives of the science study?

A careful study of a teacher's test gives a rather clear picture of what she has been trying to teach. If one gives tests that are paper-and-pencil, fill-in-the-blank type, quite likely the teaching has been the "tell-me-the-word-that-goes-in-the-sentence" type.

On the other hand, if the teacher hands out much blank paper with his tests, he has probably been the "here-is-the-situation-in-which-to-think———let's-go" type of teacher.

There is a great deal of difference between a "blank paper" and the "blanks on paper" type of test.

Re-diagnosis of a class or smaller group of children represents a key to success in planning the next step. There are several strategies which will help you in re-diagnosing a learning situation.

First, when a child suggests an explanation, probe further by responding to his explanation with "How do you know?" or "What makes that seem reasonable to you?" Don't agree or disagree with his explanation *even if you are convinced he is correct or wrong.* Help children to question whether their explanations are reasonable comments on *their* experiences; what seems reasonable to you is not as important. This is valuable technique for evaluating the progress of the child.

A second strategy involves helping the child to back up and simplify complex statements or explanations. This gives you an opportunity to find out just how neatly the puzzle has fit together for the child. Accepting complex statements because they sound good and adequate to you may result in your making a false diagnosis of where the child is and where he should move next.

Third, when a child gives you an inappropriate response, have him tell you more about the situation. Probe for the basis of an inappropriate response rather than just telling him he is wrong and then searching for the "correct" answer from someone else.

SUMMARY

Re-diagnosis of the needs of a child by comparing his performance in a new situation with the description of the desired results of a study is a means by which a teacher can decide what new experiences are needed. Based on observable evidence of the children's behavior, some may need continued experiences toward similar goals. Others may be ready for new goals.

SHARPENING YOUR CONCEPT OF EVALUATION

Evaluation may be the result of many pressures on the teacher. Boyer and Walsh describe one of these pressures—to provide equal opportunity for all; or do they really mean to categorize children as bright and dull so that we can teach or ignore them accordingly?

Another demand for evaluation is in order to report progress. Link and Chadwich *et al.* discuss this pressure on the teacher and some alternatives for coping with the pressure.

Evaluation as a means to involve the child and teacher in the game of education is described by Anderson and Kowitz.

There are many reasons that we may give for evaluating. Before reading these selections, you will find it useful to list the reasons you evaluate; and then add or modify these lists as you study these authors' opinions.

Anderson, Ronald D. "Has the Objective Been Attained?" *Science and Children*, October 1967, pp. 33–36.

Evaluation, according to Anderson, is done in order to locate learning difficulties of individual children. A second reason for evaluating is to permit the teacher to alter planned instruction. Anderson also distinguishes between formal and informal evaluation.

Boyer, William H. and Paul Walsh. "Are Children Born Unequal?" *Saturday Review*, October 19, 1968, pp. 61–63, 77–79.

The authors seem to stress the importance of the environment as a contributor to intelligence. This has obvious implications for you if you were evaluating children in an "economically depressed area" or an "economically advantaged area." If we assume that all children are capable of learning, then we should be interested in stimulating creative ability, increasing intelligence, and developing interest, and determining how these can be reflected in evaluations.

Chadwick, Ruth E., Rose Durham, and Marion Morse. "The Report Card in a Nongraded School." *The National Elementary Principal*, January 1968, pp. 22–28.

Part of evaluation is reporting progress, both to the children and to their parents. The authors describe in detail an evaluation form they developed which is a unique departure from the traditional report card.

Link, Frances R. "An Approach to a More Adequate System of Evaluation in Science." *Science Teacher*, February 1967, pp. 21–22.

Link expresses concern over the child who is not successful on a test. She suggests alternatives to forcing the child to continue to fail. Evaluation, according to Link, can be used as feedback.

CHAPTER FOCUS

1. Use one or two sentences to write what you think is the central idea of Chapter 6.

2. Review the list of suggested central ideas and identify those which are most like yours and those which are least like yours. What is the basis of the difference?

Suggested Central Ideas

1. In "Appraising Results," the teacher can tell, by observations and open-ended questioning, how well a child has achieved the goals (objectives) for the particular lesson, and if he needs further teaching, or if he is ready for new goals.

2. In educating or "leading" youngsters through experiences,

meaningful evaluation and feedback about their progress are needed, and the teacher should use this data to plan the next series of experiences more appropriately.

3. The teacher must clearly define in her own mind the goals or objectives she is trying to appraise before determining an instrument or technique to use. Appraisal should be used primarily for diagnosing or re-diagnosing a learning situation.

4. Appraising results involves three things:

a. Designing objectives which allow for testable appraising at the end to see if they were accomplished.

b. Re-diagnosing the class or group to plan your next step.

c. Evaluating your own teaching (or guidance) methods.

5. Appraisal or evaluation is used to determine how close the behavior of the children is to the learning objectives, and also to measure how effective the teaching strategies are in relation to the learning objectives.

6. It is through diagnosis and re-diagnosis that the teacher is able to see the child's progress. From this, the teacher can decide which children must be re-taught through different activities, and which have achieved the desired learning objectives.

7. The most important aspects of evaluation are determining which of the expected goals a child has met, and planning further lessons based on these results.

PART 2

Applications
for the Decision
Framework

Where Are You?

It is most difficult to come back from where you haven't been.

I feel positive toward that which I know; I fear that which is unknown.

Facilitating the learning of children in science is much like examining a walnut. Although you are interested in the nut meat inside, first you must pay attention to the shell. In a learning situation, you are very much interested in the ideas (the nut meat), but how a child feels about the learning experience completely encases and, many times, covers what he learns. How you as his teacher feel about this experience may be another covering shell.

Do you feel at ease with the ideas in the science lesson?

Do you feel comfortable with the apparatus used in the lesson?

Do you feel secure with the intended goals of the lesson?

Do you feel confident that you can handle children's inquiries and side excursions?

Where are you?

How you feel about the lesson is almost always communicated to your children; hence, the first concern that you have as a teacher is: What do I have to do? Answering that question—resolving that concern—is a first step in our approach to a science lesson.

What are the science processes or ideas I wish to have my children learn?

What are the specific objectives which will focus on the activities that I, or my children, may suggest?

What materials will, in the best way possible, connect children with the ideas or skills described in the objectives?

After you feel at ease with the science content, objectives, and materials of the lesson, you are then ready to think about your children and how they will feel in the science experience.

What problems or ideas will they generate with the materials?

What arrangement of the room will facilitate their working both with the materials and each other?

What kinds of ideas or interests will they want to pursue?

Knowing children and being able to capture their picture of the world will then help you to think about a third level of concern: How do I affect the children?

How can I make this a more positive influence?

How is my enthusiasm or boredom being communicated to the children?

How am I "coming through" to them, or how do they "read me"?

What questions or activities will I use to provide the springboard to the topic which best fits the needs of both *myself* and the *children?*

Translating the unknown and feared into the known and enjoyed is first, related to ourselves and our knowledge or feelings, second, related to the children, their knowledge and feelings, and third, related to both our and the children's interests and feelings, and how they affect each other.

Successful teachers of science have found seven steps essential and useful in order to translate the unknown into the known.

Step 1. Study the description of what the child should be able to do. A useful way to do this is to mentally picture what you would expect to see a child doing if he *has* achieved the objective. Then write a brief description of the task you would have the child do to show you that he has acquired the objective or that he needs more help.

Step 2. Scan various references or sources of ideas. Select one or two and outline the suggested activities.

Step 3. Review the activities you have outlined in Step 2. Identify the objective which is the focus for each activity. You may have more than one activity for an objective, but you should have at least one activity for *each* objective. A special note of caution is important: In many activities you will observe a variety of objectives being accomplished. But the learning experience for the child will be much more useful if the activity has a clear focus for a single objective rather than a vague mixture of many objectives.

Step 4. For an activity to come alive, you will quite likely need some material and equipment. For each activity, identify what material and equipment will be needed. You will also need to think about where you will be able to secure these materials (in the school, science room, or at the shopping center).

Step 5. It is very difficult to direct someone to a place you have never been. If you have been there, you can be much more specific in your directions, and you can anticipate problems the other person might experience. This is the key point for this step. Try the activities yourself *before* initiating them in your classroom.

Step 6. In your planning, decisions about time and space are essential. Review each activity. Estimate how much class time will be needed for the children to complete each activity. Mentally picture how you will arrange your room—for individual work, for team or small group interaction, or for total group discussion.

Step 7. As a parting step in your design of instructional experiences, you may wish to construct a similar plan of an alternative set of learning experiences for the same objective.

Just as is true when working with children, after having a variety of experiences with specifics, a pattern begins to emerge. This pattern becomes a more generalized idea to which more illustrations from specific experiences can be added. In the process of adding more specifics, a clear pattern or logic becomes part of the generalized concept.

Because you may not have had many specific experiences within which to search for patterns, it will be useful to see how others have designed experiences for children. Chapters 8, 9, and 10 are concerned with three curriculum sequences—Elementary Science Study, Science Curriculum Improvement Study, and *Science—A Process Approach*—which are designed to involve children in their individual learning experiences. In each chapter, there will be opportunities to apply the seven steps in translating the "feared" into the "enjoyed."

In the next three chapters, you will find common elements of three of the recently developed science curricula for each of these new curriculum sequences. These will be:

1. Illustrative *episodes* that have actually occurred in using the materials.

2. A brief definition of the *goals* of the curriculum.

3. A description of the *sequence* of activities included in the curriculum.

4. One *sample unit* from each curriculum to assist you in identifying what resources you may expect from the curricula.

5. Because additional preparation for each of the curricula is needed, a description of the *procedure* you will need to follow to adequately prepare to teach the units is included in this section.

6. An explanation of the *philosophy* upon which the curriculum is based is included in this section because each of the curricula selected for study has a unique way of defining science and its interaction with children.

However, it is neither feasible nor desirable to produce a single lesson that "fits" every child. You must be able to take the general ideas and adapt them to meet your interests and those of your students. Imbedded within the experiences with the curricula —the specifics—are opportunities for you to practice using the decision framework in Part One of this book.

You will have the opportunity to translate general goals into performance goals which will provide you with an outline picture of science instruction. This picture becomes more specific when performance goals are translated into child behaviors (see Chapter

3). When you work with a group of children, you will recognize that each individual has had previous experiences that cause him to react in different ways in your classroom. The children's interests differ. What they see and how they describe what they see will vary from one child to another. The variety of interests and insights which you observe in your children is also true for each teacher. Thus, for any set of child performances, there are many kinds of experiences which may be used to initiate and maintain the continuity of science learning experiences (see Chapters 4 and 5).

If children involved in the business of thinking or inquiry is your goal, then your assessment procedures should reflect this goal. Being able to describe specific ways to enmesh the child in experiences that require him to think rather than merely to repeat information is a part of the important dimension of deciding when you all have "arrived" (see Chapter 6).

A note of caution is important here. It is sometimes assumed that a recently written book describes new ideas. The ideas contained in this book are not necessarily new. In fact, in his description of education, *The Great Didactic* (1632), John Amos Comenius said:

The education I propose includes all that is proper for a man and is one in which all men who are born into this world should share. . . . Our first wish is that all men should be educated fully to full humanity; not only one individual, nor a few, nor even many, but all men together and single, young and old, rich and poor, of high and lowly birth, men and women—in a word, all whose fate it is to be born human beings; so that at last the whole of the human race may become educated, men of all ages, all conditions, both sexes, and all nations. Our second wish is that every one should be wholly educated, rightly formed, not only in a single matter or in a few or even in many, but in all things which are perfect human nature. . . .

As described in this book, science represents opportunities for successful experiences, for enjoyable feelings, and for personal satisfaction for each student, which may be a 1973 translation of

Comenius' ideas of 1632. There is a danger in having anything less than this as our goal for teaching. For example, in this same classic, Comenius wrote:

Teachers almost invariably take pupils as they find them; they turn them, beat them, card them, comb them, drill them into certain forms, and expect them to become a finished and polished product; and if the result does not come up to their expectations (and I ask you, How could it?), they are indignant, angry, and furious. And yet, we are surprised that some men shrink and recoil from such a system. Far more is it a matter for surprise that anyone can endure it at all.

Remember the challenge that Comenius gave:

Let the main objective of this our didactic be as follows, "To seek and to find a method of instruction by which teachers may teach less, but learners learn more; by which schools may be the scene of less noise, aversion, and useless labor, but of more leisure, enjoyment, and solid progress."

Let us go first, guide next, and consistently enjoy our experience in the way in which we heed the advice of Kahlil Gibran:

If he is indeed wise, he does not bid you enter the house of his wisdom, but rather leads you to the threshold of your own minds.*

Translated into the use of science in the elementary school as a way to facilitate individual learning, if we are indeed wise as teachers, we do not intend to impress upon our children how much we know of science, but rather how we can use science as a vehicle to lead each child to the threshold of his own thinking.

* From Kahlil Gibran, The Prophet. (New York: Alfred A. Knopf, Inc., 1965), p. 62. Copyright © 1965 by Alfred A. Knopf, Inc. Reprinted by permission of the publisher.

Involvement Experiences through the Elementary Science Study

To understand the Elementary Science Study, you must first enjoy the aroma of its excitement. In these descriptions of classroom episodes, you will find some windows of experiences to help you savor the aroma of children's experiences in ESS.

The description of the program, its sequences, a sample unit, and suggestions for teaching ESS units follow the episodes. The last part of this chapter is a discussion of the underlying philosophy of the program.

Episode 8.1

In a second-grade classroom, children were comparing how much different containers would hold. With a variety of containers available, one child decided that a tall slender container was about the same as a short wide container. "In what way?" questioned the teacher. He quickly demonstrated that both containers came up to about the same point on the ruler. "I see," said the teacher. But that was not the reply of the boy's neighbor. He did not think the containers were the same at all. "How about this?" he asked, pointing to the openings of the two containers. They were quite different as the ruler helped to demonstrate. The first boy shrugged—so what? But the second boy persisted. With a doubled-up fist, he declared that there was more inside the short wide container. "How much more?" the teacher inquired. The second child, with the help of a third, decided to find out by using the sink and water. They filled both containers and then sat pondering them. "What do you now know?" asked the teacher. "They are both full!" claimed the boys. "Which one holds more?" asked the teacher, to which one boy replied, "We don't know yet!" One boy emptied the slender container and poured water from the short one into it until it was full. There was still enough water in the shorter container to fill two more of the slender containers. "See, what did I tell you!"

Episode 8.2

The third-grade class had been enjoying the discoveries of how many of their feet it took to fill the doorway, the length of the room, and other spaces. They had "measured" their paper "selves" to find out how many of their feet tall they were. Doug found that he was nine "Doug feet" tall. Thus, as he moved back to his desk, someone said, "Doug, I bet your shadow isn't as tall as that." Several children used Doug's paper feet to measure his shadow, and found that it was between four and five "Doug feet" tall. Was this true for others in the class? With much enthusiasm, several children compared their shadow lengths to their paper lengths. Their shadows were about half as tall as were their paper silhouettes. As she glanced out the window, the teacher saw a shadow of a nearby elm tree. She wondered how they could find out how tall the tree was. Some suggested climbing up and measuring it. Then a girl who had been watching the teacher went to the window and looked out. "Why not measure the shadow of the old tree?" she said. "Good idea, but what would that tell us?" asked the teacher. From Doug's and others' comparisons, they concluded that the shadow was about half the real thing. In measuring the shadow, they found it to be about thirteen "Doug feet" tall, so they concluded the the tree was about twenty-six "Doug feet" tall. And they were right, for that part of the tree was about thirteen feet above the ground.

Enthusiastic in their search for shadows to measure, they also used their "shadow length" rule to measure the flagpole, the school bus, and the swing stands. Only clouds could hinder their activity.

Episode 8.3

In a fourth-grade class where the teacher was an enthusiastic fisherman, the topic of which bait was best to use was being discussed. The teacher found that many in the class really had never had much contact with worms, so she brought an empty plastic container to school. After their exploration of worms in small trays, the children put the worms into the container for further observation. The teacher wondered what kinds of things the children would be interested in learning about the worms. One child asked if the worms would stay on top or if they would go to the bottom. Another said he was sure they would go to the bottom, but he wanted to know how long it would take. A third child said he thought that if they were put in the bottom, they would come up because you find worms on top of the ground. Another child indicated that they would come up only if the top was wet or if they were hungry. Another child wondered if worms would crawl through sand, or if it would scratch them. After the children shared their ideas, they decided to put some worms on the bottom and some on the top and to put a sand layer in the middle. They also poured water in one end of the top, and then they sat back to watch. They were anticipating what was going to happen and the teacher knew that the study of worms was well in progress.

Episode 8.4

The balance board consisted of an upright dowel with a movable piece of pegboard suspended from it. It had proved a real attention-getter in a fifth-grade class. Constructing a symmetrical arrangement had been a real challenge for most of the boys and girls. Then, for fun, the teacher posed this question, "Hang one washer anywhere you want to on the board. How many different ways can you balance it?" The class was organized in pairs, and they went right to work. Some groups were satisfied with only one way to balance the pegboard. Others worked until they had two ways. Three groups found more than three ways to balance it with a single washer, such as balancing with one washer, balancing with two separate washers, balancing with two washers together, and balancing with three washers together. Intrigued with the results, the children were puzzled by the teacher's question on the board, "Can you balance with twelve washers?" Ideas began flowing. Work was in progress and twelve minutes later one group succeeded. Seven groups were still at work and five groups had given up. Patterns and puzzles with the balance board were really fun!

Episode 8.5

In an alert and active first-grade class, the teacher heard some children discussing pollution.

"What does that mean?" she inquired of them.

"Oh, junk and stuff in the water that kills animals and stuff."

"What kinds of animals in the water?"

"Oh, whales and fish, and crawdads, too." Others said that they were talking about ponds, not the oceans, so that there wouldn't be any whales, but there could be frogs and turtles. Did anyone know of a pond? One of the boys who rode the bus said they had a pond for the horses and cows at his farm. Others had never seen a pond. After a trip to visit the pond, the class brought back some water to see if there were any animals in it. The water was a brownish muddy color and hope was low that *anything* could live in that! After a day or so, someone thought they saw something move. With a large magnifying glass they could see small animals moving. So the pond water was alive after all!

But what did all this have to do with pollution? The class agreed that they had heard that detergents were a kind of pollution. Would this "soap" hurt the pond-water animals? They decided to take some of the pond water and animals out of the aquarium and put them in a smaller container and add detergent to it. Two days later, they carefully studied the two containers. The one without the detergent had many moving animals, but the detergent container seemed to have none. The children's conclusion: detergent kills animals, so mother should quit using soap. Incidentally, the teacher wondered what she would hear from parents at the next PTA meeting.

Episode 8.6

Recess was over and the sixth-grade class had settled in their seats. It was a hot muggy day and the attention span of the children was short, but today they quickly focused on a new event. In the center of the room, the teacher was placing an inverted jar over a burning candle. The candle was in a shallow dish of water. As they watched, the candle burned and the water slowly began to rise in the jar. The longer the candle burned, the more the water rose until—puff, the candle went out and the water had filled nearly one-third of the jar. Murmurs of "How come?" "Do it again," were heard in the room. Next to the candle set-up, there was another container of water with an inverted jar in it. At the top of the inverted jar was a large bunch of steel wool. After the candle experience had been repeated two or three times, someone noticed that the water in the steel wool jar was slowly rising. Why?

Although the teacher had wanted to answer directly, she asked, "What do you think is in the two jars?" Everyone agreed that there was air, but they did have many different ideas as to what kind of air. Was the air in the candle jar the same as the air in the steel wool jar? Finding the answers to these questions launched the class into a thoroughly involved and enjoyable set of investigations of gases and air.

Episode 8.7

Another sixth-grade teacher enjoyed seeing her children tackle what they thought were simple problems but which she knew were a much more difficult challenge. She arranged her class in groups of four, and had placed a large picture of a clown on the bulletin board. The task was for each member of the team to copy one-fourth of the clown picture. The results were both fun and sobering. The children put their pictures together but found that the legs didn't match, the bodies were not symmetrical, and the whole task needed to be repeated. They developed individual strategies but most of them worked out ways to draw the same size and to place the parts on paper. The second set of drawings was much more satisfactory.

The teacher then asked each group to make a map of the room. The groups started by raising questions such as, "How large will the map be?", "How big should things in the map be?", "Will we draw it as if we were looking from the door or the top of the room?", "Should we use graph paper?", and "What things are we going to put in the map?" Agreement in group decisions and follow-through was the highlight of the "Map-Making" study.

WHAT IS ELEMENTARY SCIENCE STUDY?

This study was originated for two main purposes: (1) to develop new science materials, and (2) to change the quality of science education in the schools.

The initiators of these materials were convinced that most children were not familiar with scientific thinking and were quite bored with science as they had experienced it in school. As Randolph Brown, a former director of the Elementary Science Study, stated it:

Science along with other subjects continues to be presented to students as a body of knowledge to be mastered even if not understood. Textbooks are still the main instructional vehicle and instruction is compartmented in many ways to prevent the majority of students from recognizing continuity among subjects. Teachers persist in the role of authority, a role which requires them to assign, direct, correct, and test. Lectures and reading are predominant. Class discussion too often amounts only to recitation. Questions come chiefly from the teacher. Speculation and conjecture appear rarely or not at all. Being right remains the end; obedience the means. This is not to say that efforts have not been made by the teachers or that the curriculum projects have not had important effects.*

A key member of the program, Phillip Morrison, has also stated that teaching science is more than making marks on the blackboard or talking a bit. For the scientist, the essential act is abstraction, and that is his oldest and most difficult task, and in that task are his errors as well as his victories. But it is exactly this spirit of science which books, lectures, and program texts rarely allow the child to share. Morrison also states that only the material without its manmade labels can instruct in this spirit of science, and only the errors so made by the child can lead to a real and productive understanding of the true nature of science. Instruments and laboratories, texts, and so on, force the child in a single direction to the conclusions of science. This is inexcusable because it makes the style of science far more remote to the young child than it is, in reality, for the adult scientist.

To accomplish these goals, however, David Hawkins, another member of the ESS team, has stated that ways of learning which involve the child directly with concrete experiences and which also have a built-in aesthetic reward—in that they move from play toward involvement in meaningful work—are essential for science instruction.

Designing instructional materials that *involve the student,* that *have an intrinsic, aesthetic appeal,* and that *incorporate the positive effect of play* are the three goals of the Elementary Science Study.

Morrison also described experiences as "food for the eye and the hand." He has described very vividly how our society has produced a very limited environment for children. This environment, in which as much as 70 percent of our children live today, is a suburban one. While our environment does include tremendously expanded horizons in terms of video–image and human contact, it

* From Randolph Brown, *Elementary Science Study Newsletter,* 19 (October, 1969). Reprinted by permission of the Elementary Science Study of Education Development Center, Inc.

does not provide the child with the opportunity to manipulate things, to watch living things grow, or to see cycles in nature.

To improve the commonplace experience of children, as well as to replenish it, a series of units has been developed. These units do not have specific behavioral goals because it is anticipated that different teachers with different groups of children will use them in quite different ways. The units are designed to let children experience, respond to that experience, and experience more. But because of each child's different background, how and what he responds to will vary from one child to another.

THE SEQUENCE

Imbedded in the philosophy of the development of these materials is the lack of a specific sequence. Units have been tried out at many levels and with a range of success or sophistication which

UNIT	GRADE LEVEL									
	K	1	2	3	4	5	6	7	8	9
Eggs & Tadpoles	X	X	X	X	X	X				
Brine Shrimp		X	X	X	X					
Match and Measure	X	X	X	X						
Where is the Moon?				X	X	X	X	X		
Bones					X	X	X			
Crayfish					X	X	X			
Tracks					X	X	X			
Earthworms					X	X	X			
Pond Water		X	X	X	X	X	X	X		
Mosquitoes				X	X	X	X	X	X	X
Budding Twigs					X	X	X			
Daytime Astronomy						X	X	X	X	
Mapping							X	X	X	
Butterflies	X	X	X	X	X	X				
Light and Shadows	X	X	X	X						

Figure 1.   ESS Units Emphasizing Outdoor Activity

depends upon the interest level of students, previous experience of students, and so on. For this reason, the units are better described by primary–intermediate levels rather than by grade levels. Further study of the materials indicates that those of the primary level are of two types: units requiring outdoor activities and those requiring indoor activities. Figure 1 illustrates the outdoor kind of activities, and Figure 2 the indoor kind of activities.

UNIT	GRADE LEVEL									
	K	1	2	3	4	5	6	7	8	9
Light and Shadows	X	X	X	X						
Primary Balancing			X	X						
Animals in the Classroom	X	X	X	X	X					
Growing Seeds		X	X							
Life of Beans and Seeds	X	X	X	X	X					
Pattern Blocks	X	X	X	X	X	X	X			
Printing	X	X	X	X						
Mirror Cards	X	X	X	X	X	X	X	X	X	X
Attribute Games and Problems	X	X	X	X	X	X	X	X	X	
Tanagrams	X	X	X	X	X	X	X	X	X	
Mobiles	X	X	X	X	X					
Musical Instrument Recipe Book	X	X	X	X	X	X	X	X	X	X
Geo Blocks	X	X	X	X	X	X	X			
Spinning Tables		X	X							
Changes				X	X	X				
Sand			X	X						
Structures			X	X	X	X	X			
Bulbs and Batteries					X	X	X			
Batteries and Bulbs II						X	X	X	X	X
Mystery Powders				X	X					
Whistle and String				X	X					
Ice Cubes				X	X	X				
Colored Solutions				X	X	X	X			

UNIT	GRADE LEVEL									
	K	1	2	3	4	5	6	7	8	9
Clay Boats				X	X					
Drops, Streams, and Containers				X	X					
Peas and Particles					X	X	X	X	X	
Sink or Float			X	X	X					
Optics					X	X	X			
Small Things					X	X	X			
Microgardening					X	X	X	X		
Senior Balancing					X	X				
Behavior of Mealworms						X				
Starting from Seeds					X	X				
Mapping					X	X				
Heating and Cooling						X	X			
Kitchen Physics						X	X			
Gases and Airs						X	X	X	X	
Balloons and Gases						X	X	X	X	
Pendulums						X	X	X		
Rocks and Charts			X	X			X	X	X	
Animal Activity				X			X	X		
Stream Tables					X	X	X	X	X	X
Water Flow						X	X			

Figure 2. ESS Units Emphasizing Indoor Activities

Briefly described, the individual units are as follows:

Eggs and Tadpoles (K–5)

The main purpose of this unit is to encourage children's natural interest in living things through the exploration of frog eggs and tadpoles. By observing and learning to ask questions, children gain new insights into the environment and its ecology. They start with frog eggs, and draw pictures of them, and then describe how they change. Through the ordering of pictures, they create a sequence of the life cycle of the frog, and include descriptions of many essential aspects of the frog's environment.

Brine Shrimp (1–4)

By raising brine shrimp and watching them develop, children become acquainted with some of the problems confronted by living organisms. By finding answers to questions such as, "What is that brown stuff (shrimp eggs)?", "How do you get them to hatch?", "After they hatch how do they move?", "What do they eat?", and "Where do they stay in their jar?", children learn more about both the shrimp and how to keep them alive.

Match and Measure (K–3)

In this set of activities, children use "size" words to describe how they perceive their world. Measuring devices become better understood and more valuable to the child when they are used with other tools that the child has invented to help him to describe his perceptions. A key idea of this unit is that measuring cannot be taught—it must result from exploratory experience in which matching or comparing is the method. Key questions suggested for this unit are:

"Will the tallest person's shoe fit anyone else's foot?"

"Can you tell me how tall your tower was before it toppled?"

"In your family, who is the tallest? the shortest?"

"How can you tell whether your shadow is as big as you are?"

"Is your nose as long as your thumb?"

"How much food does a pet eat?"

"How much do you eat compared with your dog?"

Where is the Moon? (3–7)

Happenings in the sky have long been important to man, but the sensible interpretation of these occurrences must begin with careful observations followed with identified reoccurrences or patterns. Seeing that the world behaves in an orderly fashion is an initial step for the child. Observing the position of the moon, describing its position in terms of a fixed point or frame of reference, and then describing the apparent path of its change during three months are several of the activities included in this unit.

Bones (4–6)

Bones are an intriguing part of the child's world but are often a mystery. How they fit together and the frustration or success in constructing a skeleton are parts of this unit. Starting with an assortment of bones, children enjoy the use of the song "Dry Bones." Describing bones is followed by assembling them into a partial skeleton. The full experience of cooking an animal and preparing its skeleton is another dimension of this intriguing study.

Crayfish (4–6)

Crayfish offer an enjoyable experience for observation in the classroom. Children can watch them find places to live, establish their right to live there, and mate. The unit provides opportunities for children to experiment with many aspects of the animal's environment—its home, its food supply, and its sleeping habits. The possible social order experiment with crayfish will be of special interest to some children.

Tracks (4–6)

The key focal point of these "animal–footprint" experiences is the explanation or interpretation possible from a single set of observations. In addition to those alternative interpretations, emphasis is on supporting interpretations with concrete observations. Questions for investigation are:

"What can you tell me about the tracks?"

"How large is the animal?"

"How does he use his feet?"

"Where does he live?"

"Where was he going when he made the tracks?"

"What happened in this picture, and what is the 'track story'?"

Earthworms (4–6)

The study of these animals provides the opportunity for the child to observe the life cycle, habits, and preferences in the behavior of the worm. Starting with a field trip to collect the worms, children investigate such questions as:

"How deep down will the worms be?"

"Are they in the same place every day?"

"How long does it take for them to dig into the dirt?"

"Do they ever burrow with their tail end?"

"What do you need to keep the worm alive?"

"What kind of environment do they prefer?"

"What kind of food do they eat?"

Pond Water (3–7)

This unit is an introduction to the exciting array of pond life and the complicated interaction between the animal and water systems. Beginning with a field trip to collect mud and water from a pond, children observe the various kinds of life and draw pictures of what they see. Then they have a variety of experiments with the animals and their feeding habits. In addition, various pond-polluting additives can be introduced. A final puzzle is posed: Do animals in pond water communicate with each other?

Mosquitoes (3–9)

This unit offers an opportunity to study the life cycle and the ecological needs of a common insect. From observations of the larvae, children investigate such questions as:

"How do larvae know which way is up?"

"Why do larvae go to the top of water?"

"Why would it be better for larvae to live in a tin can than in a pond?"

Study of adult mosquito behavior is centered around such questions as:

"How does a mosquito find you?"

"How far does it fly?"

"How do they bite?"

Budding Twigs (4–6)

In the examination of the structure of twigs—beginning with the development of buds forced into bloom out of season—children observe the complexity of plant structure. Observation of the number, arrangement, position, and covering of buds emphasizes the variations in both covering and growth characteristics, such as placement of leaves in relation to buds or flowers, sequence of leaves, and diversities on a single twig.

Daytime Astronomy (5–8)

This unit offers a delightful opportunity for the child to visualize spatial relationships and to understand several concepts of scalar model development. Through location of the sun and investigation of how its position appears to change during the day, the child is provided with a challenge through the observations of shadows. A further challenge is contained in the question: "If you live at the North Pole, would you see sunlight today?"

Light and Shadows (K–3)

Through the observation of shadows and how they change during the day, children begin involvement experience with change in spatial relationships. Making the biggest possible shadow with an umbrella and encircling a pebble with the shadow of a hand are only two possibilities in this unit. The use of mirrors is included with the challenge: "If I can see you, can you see me?"

Primary Balance (K–4)

The prime goal of this unit is to help the child gain a feeling for balance, including the concepts of weight and mass. With a balance board and an equal arm balance, children experience the answer to the question: "How much balances how much?" The relationships between weight and shape and weight and mass lead to an intriguing question: "When the board is balanced, where does the weight go?"

Growing Seeds (K–3)

From their classification of things that grow and things that do not grow, children then plant various objects. After examining changes during germination, children then record changes in the plant's height over time. Describing changes in growing plants is the key goal of this unit.

Pattern Blocks (K–6)

This unit emphasizes the spatial relationships and their related numerical relationships. Using pattern blocks, children make pictures of things, such as floor patterns. They have many opportunities to make the same shape larger, or to make new shapes. With mirrors, they can duplicate shapes. The number concepts involved include the following: span, congruity, ratio, symmetry, and angle measurement.

Printing (K–3)

This is mainly a fun type of involvement experience in which the child has an opportunity to define in words and pictures something of real and close concern to him.

Mirror Cards (5–6)

This is a logical extension of many of the ideas in the *Pattern Blocks* unit. Children have many opportunities to mess around with mirrors and cards in informal activities that result in a feeling for the physical effect of mirrors and symmetry. By using mirrors, children can create new patterns or pair series of cards through mirror matching.

Attribute Games and Problems (K–8)

This excellent unit is a skillful blending of activities that helps children develop thinking skills with problems involving classification and relationships between classes. Through a variety of experiences, children sort, map, and play take-away and question games. For example, after arranging the blocks, one block is taken away and the person identifies which one is missing. Matrix construction and its use is another feature of this unit.

Mobiles (K–4)

By constructing various types of mobiles, children can continue their experience with balance. They make mobiles which reinforce the principles of symmetry and which provide a good lead-in to the *Primary Balance* unit. Creative experiences are also encouraged.

Musical Instrument Recipe Book (K–9)

This is another set of activities that combines craftsmanship with exploration of the nature of sound and the physical properties of things that produce sounds.

Geo Blocks (K–6)

The activities of this unit give children varied experiences with geometric space and stimulate their interest in linear, surface, and volume relationships. They build with Pattern Blocks and Attribute Blocks and learn the math concepts of surface air, volume, scaling, grouping, and geometric shapes. Questions such as these are included:

"Can you make bigger ones out of little ones, or smaller ones out of bigger ones?"

"Can you make something that will not fall over easily?"

"How much 'outside' does a cube have? How can you measure it?"

Spinning Tables (1–2)

This is an intriguing set of experiences concerning objects in motion and the differences that occur when they are viewed from different angles. A unique feature of the unit is the child's experience with non-linear motion. How one predicts circular motion is a key to the enjoyable experiences of the unit. Chalk and marble activities offer a unique set of challenges for the child.

Changes (2–4)

Do all things change? Is the rate of change the same for all things? These and other questions are the focal points of this unit in which children group objects according to "change" and "not change," and then, after observation of such objects as food, rust, maggots, and rocks, children learn to regroup them according to their rate of change. A second objective is the ability to make distinctions between changes resulting in development and deterioration.

Sand (2–3)

Through a variety of activities in sorting sand, making volume comparisons, measuring, and weighing, children continue their development of an understanding of their environment. In building piles of sand and discovering how to keep it piled up, they create a need for measuring the pile. They are also challenged by the reverse question, "What can you do to get the sand to dry quickly?" Creative expression is possible in the making of sand or the making of rocks. The coloring of sand and subsequent picture-making emphasizes the versatility of this part of the child's environment.

Structures (2–6)

In this unit, children begin to understand the idea of form and purpose in engineering various structures, such as bridges. Initiated with the question, "How tall a tower can you build?", the children are challenged by the task, "What is the highest structure you can build with 50 straws and 20 pins?" Another activity is the building of a straw bridge from one desk to another and then finding out how many straw pieces can be removed before the bridge collapses.

Batteries and Bulbs (4–6)

To determine what parts of an electrical system are essential to lighting the bulb is the unique challenge of this introductory unit in electricity.

Mystery Powders (3–4)

Describing the properties of substances in the world around us is a key idea of the unit. Using various known indicators, children can observe changes which indicate the presence of a common substance. Initial activities with heat also suggest other ways to describe properties of substances.

Whistles and Strings (4–5)

This is an investigation of basic sound and how it changes through making elements of more complex musical instruments. Children develop insights into conditions necessary to produce sound and to affect pitch, tone, quality, and loudness. Activities are initiated with the question: "What can you do to get a tube to make a sound?" This can be followed by questions, such as: "How many sounds can one tube make?" "How does changing the tube change the sound?"

Ice Cubes (3–5)

In response to the question, "What makes an ice cube melt faster or slower?", children plan systematic experiments and carefully collect data. Graphs as useful communicators of conclusions are introduced.

Colored Solutions (3–6)

Density is a phenomenon of high interest to children, especially when they think they see colored solutions floating in or on other colored solutions. Using previous experiences as a basis for predicting future events is a central idea in this unit.

Peas and Particles (4–8)

While it may appear to be best to always use a direct measurement for observing, it is equally true that indirect measurements are sometimes essential. This unit demonstrates that while counting all the small particles in a large container is nearly impossible, counting those in a small container and establishing the total as a multiple of that number is a much more feasible approach.

Senior Balancing (4–6)

Based on earlier ideas in the *Primary Balance* unit, the child is introduced to weight and investigations involving force. Equilibrium, symmetry, and gravitational force illustrate the natural combination of science and mathematics. Two illustrative tasks are: "What is the lightest thing that you can weigh on the balance board?" and "Can you make a lump of clay that weighs as much as one-half of a washer?"

Behavior of Mealworms (6)

Getting a mealworm to back up is a task that immerses children in the study of this simple animal's behavior. Maintenance of the environment and design studies that lead to probabilistic answers illustrate the open-endedness of science.

Starting from Seeds (5–6)

The effect of the environment on the growth of seeds and plants is the main theme of this unit. Starting with a question, "Will seeds grow in the dark?", children investigate many possible variations in both the planting of seeds and the subsequent care of the plants.

Mapping (5–7)

Maps are descriptions that must be decoded by the user. Children can work with a variety of tasks in following directions, determining relative size, using coordinates, copying pictures, constructing a group map of a room, and drawing a map of the various routes to their homes.

Heating and Cooling (5–7)

Designing a controlled experiment with a variety of variables represents a significant task in science. This also involves the construction of predictions from given graphs. After answering the question, "What do you think will happen if you hold one of these rods over the candle flame?", the children can be confronted with the task of smothering a flame with a wire.

Kitchen Physics (6–7)

How liquids move, how they change, evaporate, stream, or drop are several of the discoveries in this unit. Analysis of the properties of liquids is an essential step in the total science repertoire of the child.

Gases and Airs (5–8)

From the investigation into the nature of air and the changes it undergoes when it interacts with other objects in the environment, the child gains an appreciation that what is, is not always what it appears to be. How a child can communicate to another child that air is real is fun and a challenge.

Balloons and Gases (5–8)

This unit is a logical extension of *Gases and Airs,* and one in which the child has the opportunity to collect gases and to describe their properties. He learns about tests that he can use to distinguish between gases. The intriguing idea that air weighs nothing when it is weighed *in air* is explored as a tool for identifying different kinds of air.

Pendulums (4–6)

To understand the physics of motion, energy, and momentum, children are given free opportunities to mess around with pendulums. They have the challenge and fun of getting the pendulums to swing together. As the pendulum stops, they can investigate the loss of motion and what occurs when there is no visible motion. The application of the principles of symmetry to pendulums is an intriguing challenge.

THE MATERIALS

The materials consist of individual topics which are published as separate units. Each of these units contains:

1. An introduction which includes a brief rationale for the topic, the suggested age levels, and other background information for the teacher.

2. Description of instructional activities for the class and other excursions that may be desirable.

3. A bibliography of relevant references for both the teacher and the child.

As an example, the unit *Sand* illustrates these three parts. The introduction describes a brief rationale for the use of colored sand in the classroom. The section on age indicates the range of age levels with which the unit has been found to be successful. Scheduling is a concern to teachers, and the approximation of time periods is indicated. How the classroom should be organized and what to expect in the actual operation of the unit are realistically described.

Introduction

That's not sand; that's little rocks.
Sprinkle the sand—it makes soft colors that way.
My sand's all gone. Why did it spill out so fast?
The sand is darker when it piles in a crease on the
sheet.
How does this get colored?
This is crunchy; this is like velvet.

Questions and comments tumble out as children work with sand. Almost every child seems to know something about sand, whether or not he has played in a sandbox or gone to a beach. Children's ideas and questions make up the body of this resource book on uses of sand in the classroom.

In the course of their work, children explore how sand feels, flows, piles, and slides. They compare sand with dirt, mud, salt, and sugar. They make sand from rocks and try to make rocks from sand. They find ways to sort sand. They use sand to time, count, measure, and weigh. They explore color and texture in the making of pictures, sculpture, and jewelry. Sand suggests a seemingly endless array of activities.

Why Colored Sand?

The colored sand comes in four grades (sizes), each grade a different color. Coloring seems to accentuate the size differences and focuses the children's attention on particle size. When children sift sand at the beach, they may be quite unaware that sand comes in many sizes and can be sorted by size. Particle size is worth examining because it greatly affects the way a material behaves. In addition, the color is aesthetically appealing and encourages imaginative exploration.

A supply of plain, uncolored sand in a mixture of the four grades is included in the *Kit* so that size can be explored apart from color. There is also an extra supply of fine, uncolored sand for use in pendulums and sand paintings.

Why Sand at All?

But why should sand be in a classroom? It is messy. It gets used up. You need quite a bit of room for it. Storage can be a problem.

One might reply that many children never see a beach. Even for those who do, the beach takes on a whole new dimension after *sand*. Perhaps the best justification is that most of the children and the teachers who have worked with it feel that *sand* is enjoyable.

It's quiet. Children can work on *sand* even during reading.

The children try their own ideas. I don't have to be always suggesting something.

Everyone has something to show or talk about. We get into very active discussions.

She finally has found something which absorbs her long enough to accomplish an entire piece of work. I can praise her legitimately. This gives her support to try things she couldn't handle before.

It made me keenly aware of every child's creativeness and the satisfaction that creating gives a child.

In addition to enjoying *sand,* children explore major concepts about what sand is; they examine subtle properties of color, size, weight, structure, and material. They try to decide whether it is a liquid (it pours), or whether it is a solid (it is hard to crush). They see how sand acts in different conditions: wet, dry, mixed, sorted, massed, and dispersed. They may see that a material which seems simple reveals considerable complexity. There are many attributes to be considered.

Artistic and mathematical explorations are an intrinsic part of *sand.* The children's impulse to feel the sand and watch it flow seems never to be satisfied. Colored sand is dribbled into patterns through fingers, cups, sieves, and straws. Sand pendulums make patterns which can be predicted with a little experience. Glue fixes sand paintings onto paper and wood. Paste and sand make a fine substance for sculpting.

Ages

Children of all ages seem to find *sand* appealing. It has been most successful with second- and third-grade classes. They find the sorting and the volume work a difficult but manageable challenge, and making sand from rocks a satisfying accomplishment. Older children become adept at measuring, weighing, and making pendulum patterns and timers.

A note to kindergarten teachers: It seems clear from trial classes that *colored* sand is not really necessary for kindergarteners. The youngest children manage well with plain sand and water, since building is their greatest interest.

Scheduling

Teachers have found several different schedules to be successful. Some have chosen to teach *sand* for six weeks in the spring, when activities can take place out-of-doors. Others, especially teachers of young children, have used *sand* all year long as part of their regular classroom activities. Some teachers bring out the equipment once a week for several hours at a time. Others let a few youngsters work for an hour or so every day, rotating the groups so that everyone has at least one chance a week. Less than forty minutes with the sand has proven insufficient; children no sooner get started than they have to clean up.

The Guide: A Resource Book

With sand in your classroom, many activities are possible. This *Guide* describes some that have been successful in trial class-rooms. Your class will probably find others that are just as valu-able and will want to pursue them.

The *Guide* is divided into two sections. "Exploring Properties of Sand" focuses on the sand itself. "Using Sand With Other Things" suggests art, math, and science activities for which sand is especially suited. You are urged to move freely between the sec-tions and among the activities within them. Many art and math ac-tivities follow naturally from explorations in the first section.

The chapters in both sections are organized the same way. Each offers questions which may suggest fruitful explorations. Children's comments and answers are included to illustrate possi-ble reactions and common points of confusion. Implications, directions, and cautionary remarks appear in a short paragraph following each question. The photographs are another source of teaching ideas and can be shared with the children.

The questions and suggestions in the *Guide* are intended to serve as a skeleton of ideas. They should not be used as lesson plans or tests or as descriptions of what children should accom-plish. You may want to add to them or ignore them altogether. One teacher wrote, "If you let the children explore with the mate-rials, the questions come out of their work, and all you have to do is discuss them."

Questions raised by the children often lead them to fruitful ex-ploration. When teachers have used their students' own terminol-ogy in charts, discussions, and experiments, the children have responded well.

The organization for activities is best when it comes from what the children do, rather than from what the *Guide* says.

Evaluating

Sand is a collection of suggestions that can be used in many ways. It is up to you to decide what your objectives are in making *sand* activities available and then to evaluate the children's work accordingly.

Many teachers listen to, observe, and record a child's activities and then analyze their records in the light of his past behavior. This can help them find out what interests the child and get some sense of his strengths and weaknesses in developing ideas independently, organizing materials, working with others.

Other teachers note whether or not, after working on an activity, a child can do a specific task or show evidence of understanding a specific idea. This has its difficulties, because many concepts take a long time to develop and are developed in unique ways by each child. It is usually not possible for children to get a specific idea at a set time or in response to a specific question.

One of the advantages of the activities in *sand* is that they offer many opportunities to get at the same idea in different ways. Since different children will usually come to the same idea at different times, evaluating their understanding must take place at different times. One teacher wrote, "As our work progresses, many children are exploring things they seemed not to notice at first. I don't have to worry whether or not they understand things right away."

Another reported, "Some children came upon insights on sorting when they were measuring volume. One child really noticed size differences when he did a sand painting (or maybe that's when I noticed he noticed)."

Since different children learn different things even when they are participating in the same activity, it probably makes more sense to keep the evaluation flexible than to try to control what each child is supposed to learn, just for the sake of convenience in evaluating.

Organizing the Classroom

The way you organize your classroom will greatly affect your success with this unit. *Sand* can be used as an activity involving the whole class. For many classes, this works best when the children carry on a variety of sand activities simultaneously. For example: two children may be working with hand lenses or with a microscope; another pair may set up wetting and drying experiments; several may want to make sand; a group may wish to act as a "factory," sifting the sand back to its original colors; while still another group mixes the colors again as they make patterns on a sheet.

Some teachers have used *sand* while other activities are going on in their classroom. A small group may work with the sand, while others work with plants, aquariums, reading, or music.

The materials in the *Kit* can be used to provide several comfortable working spaces. The muslin sheet spread on the floor with buckets of sand in the corners, and the cardboard box placed on a table or on the floor make natural places to concentrate activities. The trays can be used by partners or individuals on desks, on the floor, or out-of-doors. Activities requiring food coloring and water are best confined to one area. For this work, it may be convenient to provide a large open plastic container, such as a plastic dishpan or a child's wading pool. The cardboard box lined with plastic sheeting is also satisfactory.*

To teach the exercise, materials will be needed, and the list of those supplied in the class kit and those the teacher needs to collect are identified.

---

* *A Teacher's Guide to Sand.* (New York: Webster Division, McGraw-Hill Book Co., 1970), pp. 6–11. Reprinted by permission of the Elementary Science Study of Education Development Center, Inc.

MATERIALS *

The *Class Kit* for *sand* contains one each of the following packages,** labelled as shown:

"Red Sand"—12 lbs red sand (coarse)

"Yellow Sand"—12 lbs yellow sand (medium-coarse)

"Green Sand"—12 lbs green sand (semi-fine)

"Blue Sand"—12 lbs blue sand (fine)

"Mixed Grades of Natural Sand"—12 lbs mixed (coarse, medium-coarse, semi-fine, and fine) uncolored sand

"Fine Natural Sand"—12 lbs fine, uncolored sand

"Sieves for Sand"—3 each of 3 different meshes

"Multi-Purpose Balance"—one balance

"Equipment for Sand"—

1 sandbox	100 cups with lids
1 liner for sandbox	1 muslin sheet (to work on)
8 1-gallon buckets	5 containers
15 cardboard trays	4 hand lenses
200 paper cone cups	1 plastic tube with caps
50 plastic cone cups	

In addition, you may want to collect the following materials:

---

1 ball of string	shirt cardboards
2 measuring (trundle) wheels (1-foot and 1-yard circumferences)	assorted textures, colors, and sizes of paper
Oak-tag	watercolors
	paintbrushes

---

* *A Teacher's Guide to Sand.* (New York: Webster Division, McGraw-Hill Book Co., 1970), p. 13. Reprinted by permission of the Elementary Science Study of Education Development Center, Inc.

** The *Class Kit* or any of the individual packages is available from the Webster Division of McGraw-Hill Book Company, Manchester Road, Manchester, Missouri 63011.

crayons, dye, lipstick
bags (paper or plastic)
rulers
paper clips
clothespins
masking tape
scissors
soft wire or coat hangers
microscope—15 X (power) or less
funnels
assorted sieves: strainers, colanders, netting, stockings, etc.
yardstick
clay
collected sand
seeds
sugar, salt, other grainy substances
cinnamon
rocks, bricks
hammer

waxed paper, aluminum foil, cloth
nail, awl, ice pick
hook to screw into ceiling
magnets
glue (white glue, such as Elmer's Glue, is especially useful)
wheat paste
wallpaper paste
cornstarch
flour
dry cement mix
additional containers, bottles, jars, juice cans
hot plate
push broom
newspaper
sponges
food coloring
dustpan and brush
smocks

Instructional activities describe ways in which teachers can involve children with the materials. Photographs and typical child responses are used to help the teacher to gain a feeling for how the experience might go.

EXPLORING PROPERTIES OF SAND

Materials

for the class working as a group:
    muslin sheet
    cardboard sandbox

8 buckets, two of each color one-third filled with colored sand

for each pair of children working separately:

1 tray with four paper coffee cups, each half-filled with a different color of sand

---

Before You Begin

Keep the uncolored sand, food coloring, measuring wheels, yard-stick, glue, and sieves out of sight for later use. If the children see the sieves early in their work, they will be less likely to invent their own sorting devices.

WARNING: Once mixed, the uncolored and colored sand cannot be separated.

A Way To Start

One teacher started her class by gathering the children around to watch a "mystery material" flow from a cup and form a multicolored pattern on the muslin sheet. Another gave each child a pinch of colored sand to examine.

One method for getting the children used to working in different ways is to start them off in separate groupings about the room, each pair of children with a supply of sand and tray to work on.

What is it?

Jello mix.
It feels like rice.
Fake rocks.
It's sand; I tasted it.
It's not sand; it's just little rocks.

Children will examine what sand is—its properties and composition—throughout the study. They will have conflicting theories and will have many opportunities to test them.

Note: Sand is difficult to define. Sand *is* "just little rocks," and it is also just big particles of silt or clay. Some specialists define it as mineral particles between $1/16$mm and 2mm in diameter. What is important is that sand, which at first glance seems so clearly a particular thing, can be any mineral or composition of minerals ground naturally by wind, water, weathering, and tumbling to a particular size range.

Materials

---

colored sand
muslin sheet
cardboard sandbox
trays
paper cone cups
* scissors

Flowing Sand

What does sand feel like?

The children sprinkle sand from their fingertips or let it flow through holes in the bottoms of the cone cups.

How can you keep the sand flowing?

It won't come out.

The size of the sand particles determines the size of the opening that is needed. To make wider paths and bigger hills, children may change the size of the openings by cutting the tips of the cones. Some may use fingers to stop and start the flow of sand.

What does a falling stream of sand look like?

It looks like a spray. Mine splashes.

Where do the big grains fall? Where do the small grains fall?

* *Not included in* Kit.

Building and Piling

If you build with sand, will it stay?

When you make a hole with your finger in a pile of dry sand, it fills up again.

If you build with the big sand, it stays pretty still.

You can blow the little sand into ripples and piles.

Which makes a steeper hill, big or little sand?

Piles of equal volumes of big, little, and mixed sand can be compared.

How can you measure a hill of sand?

If this question comes up, let the children who are interested try lots of ways to measure.

Put a ruler across it, and see what it says.

You have to stick something in it, like a pencil.

If you put glue on the pencil and stick it in, you can see how far up the sand comes.

Put a string around it, and see how fat the pile is.

Which can be packed harder, a pile of big sand or a pile of small sand?

Materials

colored sand	* straws
cardboard trays	* containers
cone cups	* pencils
cardboard sandbox	* water
plastic sheet	* ruler
(liner for cardboard box)	* string
	* glue

Sand and Water

Can you make a bigger pile if you wet the sand? What happens when the pile dries?

* *Not included in* Kit.

It shrinks!

Some children are astounded to see that their creations of the day before have collapsed as the sand dried.

What can you do to get the sand to dry quickly?

Pile it up.

Spread it out.

Heat it on the radiator.

Let them experiment with the method they consider best.

What happens to sand when you pour water on it?

The blue sand looks like balls of mercury.

The pile of small sand looks like quicksand.

The water just goes through the big sand.

Try drips of water. Try a steady stream. Make a sloping bed of sand in the cardboard box. Watch where different particles of sand move in a stream of water. Try making two streams . . . a dam . . . a beach . . . etc.

Will a full cup of tiny grains hold as much water as a full cup of big grains?

Some children think that there is more air space around the big grains and so a cup of them will hold more water. Although each should, in theory, hold the same amount of water, usually a cup of small grains will hold *more* water, because air stays trapped around the large grains and takes up some of the space.

Will the color come off in water? Can you get it off?

The children can experiment with color that *will* come off, by adding food coloring to uncolored sand.

Will the color come off when you add water to sand made from a red brick?

Does sand dissolve?

Mix cinnamon with sugar to look like colored sand. Color some fine sand to look the same. (Use a few drops of red and yellow food coloring.) Don't tell which is which, but put both the sand and the cinnamon mixture in water.

Will sand ever melt?

Attempts to dissolve sand may lead to questions about melting it. Some classes may want to try melting sand in connection with a study of how sand is used in making glass.

Materials

sand	* homemade sieves (stockings, netting, colanders, strainers)
plastic tube and stopper	
paper cups	
sieves (keep them out of sight until the children have attempted to make their own sorting devices)	* waxed paper, aluminum foil, cloths of different textures
	* paintbrushes
* pencils	* paper clips
* cardboard	* clothespins

Sorting Sand **

After the children have been building and drawing with the colored sand, there is usually a big container of mixed sand. This poses a new problem.

How can the sand be separated?

It's all mixed up. How can we get it unmixed?
I need more yellow, and there isn't any left.

Let the children try to solve the problem themselves. Often they start separating sand by picking out the large particles. Some find that a paintbrush helps sort the grains.

Is there a way to do it faster?

Some children invent machines to make sorting more efficient. Encourage them to bring in things to try. A comb makes a good separator.

What does a sieve do?

At first, children tend to use the sand and sieves in a haphazard way. Later, some children may notice that certain sieves work better than others and that some colors will not go through the sieve they are using. They may trade sieves and colors of sand and notice different results. Finding a relationship between the

* *Not included in* Kit.

** *A Teacher's Guide to Sand.* (New York: Webster Division, McGraw-Hill Book Co., 1970), pp. 15–21. Reprinted by permission of the Elementary Science Study of Education Development Center, Inc.

sand and the hole size of each sieve takes time and experience. Many are perplexed to have three sieves for four sizes.

Note: Don't be concerned that the two largest sizes of sand won't separate clearly into the original colors. The larger the particles, the greater is the variation in size that comes through a screen.

How many sizes can you separate with two sieves? . . . three sieves?

We have a factory. I get the red out of the blue–green–yellow and give it to Danny. He gets the yellow out and gives the blue–green to Shirley, and she gets the green out from the blue.
The red won't go through any sieve.

On Friday afternoon Kevin and I sifted out the sand. First I used the blue sifter and sifted out the blue sand from the mixed and then I used the green sifter and sifted green from yellow and red. Then I took the yellow sifter and sifted yellow from red and I had red in the yellow sifter.
By Ginny and Debbie *

Extension or side excursions are described for those children who wish to pursue the subject further.

Materials

sand
** Oak-tag
** cardboard
** heavy paper
** glue (white glue, such as Elmer's Glue, mixed with water to make it go further works well)
** paste

* *A Teacher's Guide to Sand.* (New York: Webster Division, McGraw-Hill Book Co., 1970), pp. 15–21. Reprinted by permission of the Elementary Science Study of Education Development Center, Inc.
** *Not included in* Kit.

MAKING SANDPAPER *

This is one activity which might be done early if there are children who need to see a use for their work or want something to keep.

The effect that sandpaper has on materials is a function of the size, shape, and hardness of the sand particles used.

How is sandpaper made?

What kinds of sandpaper can you make?

The sandpaper can be any size, shape, color, or thickness the children want. It can be made with a light sprinkling of sand or with sand put on thickly. Homemade, plain, or colored sand can be used.

What happens to the things you sand? What happens to the sandpaper?

This rock is too hard to sand. All the sand is worn off my sandpaper.

What makes different sandpapers?

Children may bring in many different samples of sandpaper. They can scrape sand off the surface of the coarse sandpaper and look at the grains under the magnifying glasses, comparing them with other sand grains they have seen.

Is sand the only material that makes rough paper?

Some materials that children may suggest are salt, sugar, rice, chalk dust, seeds. They can make "sandpaper" with each of these and try sanding with it.

SAND PENDULUMS *

What patterns are made when sand flows from a swinging cup?

Sand flowing from a cup or funnel swinging like a pendulum leaves patterns of the pendulum's motion.

How can you hang a sand pendulum?

* *A Teacher's Guide to Sand*. (New York: Webster Division, McGraw-Hill Book Co., 1970), pp. 46–47. Reprinted by permission of the Elementary Science Study of Education Development Center, Inc.

Here are some ideas:

- Suspend a string from a hook in the ceiling.
- Suspend a string from two hooks in the ceiling.
- Suspend a pendulum from a doorway.
- Suspend a string between two desks from a yardstick raised by piles of books. Attach it to a paper or plastic cone cup or a juice can.
- Just hold a yardstick with a cup hung from it.

Sometimes designing and building a sand pendulum is as interesting as watching the patterns it makes.

(When the children puncture a hole in the can, be sure they go from the inside out, so the sand will flow smoothly and not catch on the edges of the hole.)

How can you change the patterns?

Put it lower.

No, higher.

It looks like an egg.

It's a canoe—y shape.

I made a circle.

Try making a straight line. The children can experiment with different ways of suspending the string to see if it changes the pattern.

What happens when you use different sizes of sand in a pendulum?

Use the fine; you can see it better.

The big sand runs out too fast because the hole is so big.

Try all the colors.

Color the fine sand lots of different colors, and put each color in a cup in layers. Then let it go.

Can you use materials other than sand?

Try such things as rice, salt, sugar, flour, seeds.

Try a water pendulum out-of-doors.

Materials

fine sand	* wire (coat hangers)
plastic or paper cone cups	* juice cans
* string	* nail, awl, or ice pick
* scissors	* hook screwed into ceiling
* yardstick	* tape
* paper clips	

BIBLIOGRAPHY **

The bibliography is an annotated list of references for both the teacher and the children.

For the Teacher

Adler, Irving, *Dust*. The John Day Company, New York, 1958.

In Ch. 5, the author discusses jumping grains of sand and the formation of ripples. He also deals with how sand hills move and talks about singing sand.

Bagnold, R. A., *The Physics of Blown Sand in Desert Dunes*. Dover Publications, Inc., New York, 1941.

An authoritative study of how wind moves sand.

Bascom, Williard, *Waves and Beaches: The Dynamics of the Ocean Surface*. Doubleday and Company, Inc., New York, 1964. (Science Study Series.)

Ch. IX deals with beaches and describes the different types of beach materials and the forces that work on the sands to cause both seasonal and long-term shifting. Some nice photographs show the sand patterns left by the tides.

Carson, Rachel, *The Edge of the Sea*. Houghton Mifflin Company, Boston, 1955.

---

* *Not included in* Kit.
** *A Teacher's Guide to Sand*. (New York: Webster Division, McGraw-Hill Book Co., 1970), p. 48. Reprinted by permission of the Elementary Science Study of Education Development Center, Inc.

In Ch. IV, "The Rim of Sand," the author deals with the origins of the sand and its components, movements of the sand, and animals of the shores.

Nuffield Foundation, *I Do, and I Understand*. John Wiley & Sons, Inc., New York, 1967.

A rationale for, and several excellent descriptions of ways of, organizing classrooms so that a variety of activities can go on simultaneously. Also some of the activities described may go very well with the activities in *sand*.

Pond, Alonzo W., *Deserts, Silent Lands of the World*. W. W. Norton & Company, Inc., New York, 1965.

See Ch. 3, "Bouncing Grains Make Dunes of Sand," for a concise description of the formation of dunes.

Ronan, Colin A., "Making Shapes by Swings." *Nature and Science*, Vol. 2 (Nov. 2, 1964), pp. 2, 13–15.

A magazine article on sand pendulums for children.

Shelton, John S., *Geology Illustrated*. Drawings by Hal Shelton, W. H. Freeman and Company, San Francisco, 1966.

Part III. #17 is an excellent chapter on barkhans (sand dunes)— how they are formed and changed. The photographs are informative as well as beautiful. On p. 41 there is a particularly interesting microscopic comparison of sand formed by wind, and sand formed by the sea.

Villaseñor, David, *Indian Sandpainting of the Greater Southwest*. Naturegraph Company Publishers, Healdsburg, California, 1963. ($1.00—ordered directly from publisher.)

Lovely photographs and descriptions of the ancient art of painting with sand.

White, Laurence B., Jr., *Life in the Shifting Dunes*. Museum of Science, Boston, 1960.

Spending a summer on Castle Neck, Ipswich, the author discovered many natural phenomena of the area and the sands.

For the Children

Amos, William H., "The Living Sand." *National Geographic*, Vol. 127, No. 6 (June, 1965), pp. 820–833.

The author took his children to the beach, and, together, they explored the Henlopen Dunes in Delaware. He discusses how the dunes were formed and are changing and talks of his children's enjoyment of the animals, tracks, beach plants, and the wind. Excellent color photographs.

Clemons, Elizabeth, *Tide Pools and Beaches*. Alfred A. Knopf, Inc., New York, 1964.

Although there are many inaccuracies in the biology and some pretentious science, this is a nicely illustrated guide for a trip to the beach. See the chapter on "Rocks, Pebbles, and Shifting Sands."

Engel, Leonard, and the Editors of LIFE, *The Sea*. Time, Inc., New York, 1967.

See pp. 96–97, "How Beaches Are Made," for a simply written description of how sand is deposited and removed by the sea on a California beach during the course of a year.

Farjeon, Eleanor, "Sand," in *Eleanor Farjeon's Poems for Children*. J. B. Lippincott Company, Philadelphia, 1951.

McFall, Christie, *Wonders of Sand*. Dodd, Mead & Company, Inc., New York, 1966.

The author talks about what sand is, how it is formed and how it forms beaches, how it moves, and what animals inhabit the sands. The book contains some nice photographs, maps, and drawings.

Milne, A. A., "Sand-Between-the-Toes," in *When We Were Very Young*. E. P. Dutton & Company, Inc., rev. ed., New York, 1961.

Stevenson, Robert Louis, "At the Seaside," in *A Child's Garden of Verses*. Charles Scribner, New York, 1905.

TO TEACH ESS MATERIALS

To adequately prepare for the teaching of an Elementary Science Study unit, in our opinion, six specific steps are essential:

First, read the unit guide carefully to identify the science concepts involved. In many of these units in the introductory section, activities are suggested for the teacher to do. While it is easier to read and not *do* these activities, you will find that doing them yourself will really pay off in your understanding of the scientific ideas.

Second, study the activities and construct your own outline of what your children will be doing in each activity. For each activity, you will find it very helpful to specify the child behaviors or performance objectives. This will help give focus to each activity and assist you in visualizing the sequence of ideas and activities in the room.

Third, for each activity identify which materials will be needed and when they will be used. Are they supplied or will you need to secure them? Do the materials need to be set out ahead of time or is there any previous organization necessary?

Fourth, do the actual child activity yourself first. You will find this step essential to have a reasonable expectation of time. If it calls for seeds to germinate, do it and see how many days it takes for seeds to germinate in your area. If it calls for ice cubes to melt, try it and find out whether it requires one hour or two days. Your confidence in being an effective guide for children's learning will be directly related to your confidence in knowing what to expect from the situation. Omitting the fourth step can be very disastrous.

Fifth, study the suggestions of how to arrange the children in your room. Rethinking the activities may suggest that you will need to revise the planned room arrangement or grouping.

Sixth, for each activity, write out what you will say or do to initiate child involvement or direct their thinking in a discussion. Most of the activities will have excellent suggestions which you will find quite useful in involving children in exciting and meaningful experiences.

WHY ESS?

That science is important to our world, no one can deny. That most of our world is alienated from science and picture it as a forbidden monster is all too true. To make science a meaningful and enjoyable experience is the key purpose of ESS. In ESS, much attention has been given to the child, how he learns, and how he acquires language.

A child's habits and styles of thinking and his attitude toward learning are markedly influenced by the conditions under which learning takes place. If speculations about the psychology of learning are to be useful in education, they must take into account a wide range of problems, including the subtle and complex problems of classroom organization. While certain experiences may be more useful than others in helping children develop effective skills of thought, and while we hope that the present materials make it possible for many children to have such experiences, we must point out that simply administering a set of exercises to children without taking into account their individual interests and stages of development is unlikely to produce lasting effects. Experiences which result in growth cannot be handed to a child; they are something which he must reach out for and the opportunity for reaching may require conditions quite different from those in which mere passive reacting is sufficient to meet expectations.

Thinking: out of school and in

Babies and young children play, and we play with them. We do not attempt to teach them in a formal sense, and yet in an environment where there are interesting things and responsive people they learn a tremendous amount, largely on their own initiative. When they are directly involved in an activity the attention span of young children is much longer than we normally expect in the classroom and the intensity of their engagement in the task at hand is often quite astonishing. A child's play is his work, a serious and compelling work for which he uses any materials which may be available. The young child has an active mental life; he seems to be learning necessary and useful things much of the time. In his imagination he creates stories, fantasies which parallel or anticipate the real world.

Language is a most impressive intellectual acquisition, yet children learn to talk without formal instruction. The child does the work for himself, paying attention at first randomly, then in more selective fashion to the elements which seem important because of repetition or the context in which they occur. He rehearses what he needs to remember, often in a monologue at bedtime. Though learning to talk is an impressive accomplishment, almost all children do learn. In our present state of knowledge about learning, if we attempted to teach children to talk, using the traditional practices of formal instruction, they would probably never learn. In view of their great potential for learning, any attempt to help children with their thinking must be undertaken with humility, restraint, and respect.

The conditions under which young children learn so much are approximated in some of our nursery schools and kindergartens. In the best of these there is respect for the dignity of the child: his right to learn and his right to choose what he wishes to work on at a particular moment are protected. Under such conditions, the child's capacity for self-direction, his ability to become deeply involved in what he is doing, and his readiness to respond to meaningful interventions by adults and other children, are much greater than is commonly realized.

By the time a child is six years old and entering first grade, the conditions under which he is expected to learn change radically. Unfortunately, the pattern in the primary years is increasingly one of formal instruction with most of the choices about content and approach made by the school and the teacher. The teacher, with the aid of the timetable and the curriculum, assumes responsibility for teaching the child, and equates teaching with learning—a most dangerous and misleading equation.*

The responsibility for learning is thus said to belong to the child.

Much of the child's potential for learning is lost as soon as someone else attempts to assume responsibility for that learning. The child may or may not be interested in what is taught or in the way it is presented, whereas formerly he was

* Teacher's Guide for *Attribute Games and Problems.* (New York: Webster Division, McGraw-Hill Book Co., 1968), pp. 80–81. Reprinted by permission of the Elementary Science Study of Education Development Center, Inc.

able to teach himself by acting upon his immediate interests. He may learn to pay attention at least part of the time to please the teacher, or to avoid punishment, but he may lose much of his capacity to become deeply absorbed, and his attention span may become a fraction of what it was when he was working on something of his own choosing. The child who can be incredibly persistent in his spontaneous play finds himself in a situation where the only kind of persistence permitted him is that which is applied to an assigned task. If he does become interested in a school activity he must make his interest conform to the schedule of the classroom, putting away the things he is working on and beginning something else many times a day. He learns slowly to conform to the schedule and the discipline of the classroom by setting aside his own interests and learning the game called "school." The kind of self-discipline and personal involvement which enabled the child to acquire language becomes secondary to the discipline of the schoolroom and to the completion of fragments of assigned work.*

School is likened to a game in which the players must have a good memory and are interested in pleasing others. In the activities of ESS, it is most important to emphasize that the problems are not memory situations, but rather situations in which reasoning ability is called for.

In many school settings memory is often crucial, and the child with a good memory may be able to succeed with very little real thought or insight. Confronted with a new problem, however, or a rearrangement of an old one, the child who is accustomed to relying on memory may be at a loss. His thinking is often as linear as his instruction has been, the steps he has followed have little relationship to one another, and he may have little notion of where he is going or

* Teacher's Guide for *Attribute Games and Problems*. (New York: Webster Division, McGraw-Hill Book Co., 1968), p. 81. Reprinted by permission of the Elementary Science Study of Education Development Center, Inc.

where he has been. We believe that this is not a necessary pattern for education.*

In school, and in science, there are two kinds of thinking—simultaneous and sequential.

In complex situations we often deal with quantities of information virtually simultaneously, without conscious, analytic thought. We perform complex physical acts such as riding a bicycle, driving a car, or swimming, without analyzing the separate components of the acts or being able to explain in words how these components are related. We do the same when we perform complex acts which are not physical. For example, we are all able to recognize people we have seen before, without having to stop to consider their individual features.

Consider this last example. It really is remarkable that we are able to recognize hundreds of people all having two eyes, two ears, a nose and a mouth. Unless an individual has outstanding features we may find it quite impossible to describe him enough for someone else to recognize him. It is not simply the shape of the nose, the expression of the mouth, or the color of the eyes which triggers recognition. It is, rather, our simultaneous awareness of these and many other cues which gives us a virtually instantaneous impression of a unique individual. We seem to be able to handle a deluge of information at once; our thinking is so swift that we may be completely unaware of how it is proceeding.

Most of the time it is not necessary to analyze the things we do easily and naturally. Analysis becomes important when performance falters or when we wish to become consciously aware of the reasons for the conclusions we reach, or to communicate these reasons to others. Then we must be able to isolate bits of information which we have acted upon and deal with them one at a time, *sequentially.*

* Teacher's Guide for *Attribute Games and Problems.* (New York: Webster Division, McGraw-Hill Book Co., 1968), p. 82. Reprinted by permission of the Elementary Science Study of Education Development Center, Inc.

We can apparently either deal with many ideas at the same time, unreflectively, or we can separate and analyze the components of a situation, dealing with them one at a time. We cannot think in both ways at once, since focusing on isolated aspects of a situation tends to destroy our awareness of the whole. What we do, however, is to shift attention rapidly back and forth from the whole to its parts, thinking simultaneously or sequentially as required.*

As a summary of the philosophy of the units of ESS, free play is emphasized; long periods of directed teaching are avoided. "Children-designed" approaches are desired more than conventional adult-accepted strategies. Exploration with the unknown and opportunities to be creative in his approach to situations that interest him are the keystones in ESS materials.

THE DEVELOPMENT OF ESS

Early in the curriculum, reform of secondary school science was the development of the Physical Science Study Committee. As a logical extension of the interest of scientist and educator teams in the instruction in public schools, the Elementary Science Study was begun in 1960. Within the guidance and the development of Educational Services Inc., the Elementary Science Study materials were generated in summer conferences, developed in classroom exploration to see how children responded to a variety of experiences, and finally documented in trial editions of teaching units.

In 1965, sample units were sent out in the first large-scale field test. Results of this led to the revision and commercial publication of the materials in 1966. Support for the development of the materials for the ESS program has come mainly from the National Science Foundation.

* Teacher's Guide for *Attribute Games and Problems*. (New York: Webster Division, McGraw-Hill Book Co., 1968), pp. 82–83. Reprinted by permission of the Elementary Science Study of Education Development Center, Inc.

After the impact of the children and teacher, the unit is prepared for commercial publication. The criteria of this final step are that the unit must be scientifically accurate, understandable by both teachers and children, and incorporate a significant dimension in the child's science experiences.

Involvement Experiences through the Science Curriculum Improvement Study

As a springboard to searching the Science Curriculum Improvement Study curriculum, this chapter contains experiences several teachers have had in using the curriculum with children.

A description of the curriculum, its sequences, a sample unit, some suggestions for teaching SCIS, and a discussion of its philosophy follows the episodes.

Episode 9.1

The first-graders were busy during their science time with piles of substances on their trays. They had already described how the cubes of sugar and the piles of sugar were different—the cubes had sugar stuck together, while the powder wasn't stuck together. How these two piles were similar was another problem. They finally agreed that the teeny bits of stuff were all sugar. When asked for their evidence, they said that the cubes could be broken up into little bits like the powder. With a mortar and pestle, the teacher showed them how to do this. A new substance was then introduced—rock candy. Initially, the children thought it was more like the cube than the powder. One suggested that if it were broken into teeny bits, it would be more like the powder. He tried to do this with the mortar and pestle, and before long the three piles of powder sugar, smashed-up-cube, and smashed-up-candy looked very much alike!

Episode 9.2

A mystery box was the point of everyone's attention. As the second-graders were seated in a large circle around their teacher, they could all see the box on her lap. As she moved the handle on one side of the box, a flag moved on the other side. Quickly the children observed that the teacher was moving only one handle, and yet the flag also moved. Why? As possible reasons, someone suggested that the handle and flag were connected in some way. Someone else thought it might be like a bicycle. Since most children seemed satisfied with these two ideas, each pair of children was given an assortment of pulleys, rubber bands, a box, a flag, and a handle. Their task was to make their own mystery box that acted just like the teacher's. Some found that the size of the pulley and rubber band was very important. Together, the class listed objects in the system necessary to get an interaction like the teacher's —a large pulley, a small pulley, a large rubber band, the handle, the flag, and the box. Someone suggested that a boy or girl was also needed in the system.

Episode 9.3

A girl rushed over to her neighbor to tell her the news. Something was eating the daphnia in the aquarium. Earlier, the teacher had added hydra and gammarus to three of the aquaria in the room. The other three aquaria were unchanged. Several others started checking the different aquaria. Sure enough, Bill's aquarium had daphnia all over it, and so did Doug's and Janice's. But Annette's, Mike's, and Shirley's all seemed to have no daphnia. Where had the daphnia gone? Listening to the conversation, their teacher suggested that they have a conference to consider the evidence. The children quickly gathered around her. They all agreed that there had been daphnia in all six of the aquaria. They also had observed that the daphnia were still in three of the aquaria. In the other three, there were almost no daphnia—but weren't those the aquaria in which the teacher put the hydra and gammarus? So that's the reason—but, cautioned the teacher, is it? What is your evidence? What could we do to make sure? Together the class designed a way to check out their conclusion about daphnia and hydra. They would set up two aquaria—one with just daphnia and one with both daphnia and hydra, and then watch what happened.

Episode 9.4

In an animated discussion about their germination experiments in the fourth grade, the children had observed bean and clover seeds germinate. Greg had raised an interesting question. He had accidentally spilled some clover seeds into the bean container, and neither the bean nor clover seeds had germinated as well. Would mixing seeds affect the interaction of their system? To gather evidence, the group decided they would need several systems—one with just clover seeds and water; another with just beans and water; a third with a mixture of beans and clover. Then an interesting question was raised—did the number of seeds make a difference in the interaction? Suppose they put just one bean seed with many clover seeds, or many bean seeds and few clover seeds. The teacher set up stations where seeds, seed boxes, and water would be available the next day so the students could explore this question further—do seeds affect each other when they germinate?

Episode 9.5

The fifth-grade class had been busy investigating salt, tea bags, and water. They had put salt in the empty tea bags and then allowed the salt to dissolve in containers of water. After the salt had dissolved, it seemed that there were layers in the liquid. They found that if they carefully took some of the liquid at the bottom of the container in a dropper and dropped it on the top liquid layer, they could see a wavy motion down through that layer. The children had identified the objects in their system as salt, tea bag, container, and water. The interacting objects were salt and water.

After inventing the term, *phase of matter,* which she explained meant uniform materials that look and act alike, the teacher asked them what they thought a solution was. Together, they agreed that a solution was a phase that has two or more substances in it, like salt and water. While they had all made salt–water solutions, the children wondered if the layers in the containers were the same. Some said yes while others said no. The teacher then posed this question: "How can you make two solutions that act alike?" This proved to be a difficult task. Some suggested that they would need to use the same amount of salt and water. But how are salt and water measured? Another said that he thought the drop test would have to be used to be really sure. The teacher thought to herself that the next day would be a fun day with her "embryo scientists"!

WHAT IS SCIENCE CURRICULUM IMPROVEMENT STUDY?

SCIS is a course content improvement project located at the University of California in Berkeley. It is one of the projects supported by funds from the National Science Foundation. The director of this project is Robert Karplus, a professor of physics. In describing the general goal of the program, its directors have said:

The Science Curriculum Improvement Study program speaks to children in their own language. It is a language of exploration and discovery; of sensory perceptions and imagination—the language from which all human knowledge derives.

The skillful introduction of a wide variety of physical materials and living organisms invites children to feel, touch, manipulate, observe, comment and hypothesize about the mosaic that is science.

Through this involvement, primary and intermediate grade children learn major scientific concepts. Their thinking advances from what is to what could be, from fact to theory, from concrete to abstract. They begin to be scientifically literate, able to understand and evaluate scientific information addressed to laymen.*

According to its developers, the approach to instruction is a significant factor in the child's acquisition of scientific literacy. In instruction, content experiences from both physical and life sciences are organized around three types of experiences: exploration, invention, and discovery.

Exploration is the child's initial experience with the world around him.

Exploration involves the initial physical and mental contact that children have with some aspect of the natural world. For example, early in the SCIS life science program, children are provided with a number of aquaria. They are encouraged to examine these and observe any changes that may take place in the aquarium. Children may respond in a variety of ways as they observe their aquaria. One group of children, somewhat to the surprise of the adults present, raised a question about the material at the bottom of the aquarium, and this led to the experimentation with this material and the investigations of the differences between sand, salt, sugar, sponge, and chopped-up glass. It is important to note that these experiments grew out of the direct exploratory experiences that the children had had with the aquaria. Usually, it is important that children have a chance to look at, feel, and explore the materials that are to be investigated. From these explorations we often get important clues for the development of further activities with children.**

Following the exploration experience, it becomes essential for terms to be invented.

* Science Curriculum Improvement Study: An Innovative Science Program for the Elementary School. (Chicago: Rand McNally and Company, 1970), p. 1. Reprinted by permission of the publisher.
** Reprinted with permission from *SCIS Elementary Science Sourcebook*. Written and published by the Science Curriculum Improvement Study. Copyright 1968 by the Regents of the University of California.

Invention is the introduction of a new concept. After seeing the salt dissolved in water while sand did not, a chite asked, "Could the fish in the freshwater aquarium live in the salt weer?" The teacher introduced (invented) the concept of *habitat*. It was explained that habitat is the place where organisms live. A freshwater aquarium can be the habitat for certain kinds of organisms and a marine aquarium is a saltwater habitat for other kinds of organisms. Sometimes, children arrive at concepts. For example, one group was considering the number of eggs produced by frogs. They considered what would happen if all frog eggs matured into adult frogs. "Frogs would inherit the earth," one child said. This youngster apparently had achieved some concept of biotic potential. In a science program one of the very important functions of the teacher is the process of invention in which important ideas and concepts are introduced which help give meaning to the variety of experiences that children have had.*

Experiences followed by the invented terms need to have application in other situations to be fully meaningful. This third task is labeled *discovery*.

In the *discovery* phase children discover new and different instances of a concept. For example, after the invention of the concept of habitat, children can identify different kinds of habitats, consider differences and similarities, and find what kinds of organisms live in various kinds of habitats. The discovery experiences that children have serve to reinforce, refine, and enlarge upon the content of the concept that has been invented.*

THE SEQUENCE

With the materials that are presently available, the sequence of the SCIS program can be pictured as follows:

* Reprinted with permission from *SCIS Elementary Science Sourcebook*. Written and published by the Science Curriculum Improvement Study. Copyright 1968 by the Regents of the University of California.

GRADE LEVEL	PHYSICAL SCIENCE	LIFE SCIENCE
6th grade	Models: Electric and Magnetic Interactions	Ecosystems
5th grade	Energy Sources	Communities
4th grade	Relative Position and Motion	Environments
3rd grade	Systems and Subsystems	
2nd grade	Interaction and Systems	
1st grade	Material Objects	Organisms

Other units for the intermediate grades are under development. Experiences and ideas both within and between units have been selected to fit what is essential to the science–conceptual development of the child and what is appropriate to the child's thinking potential.

For the first grade, there are two units: *Material Objects* and *Organisms*. *Material Objects* includes:

Common objects and special materials provided in the kit are described by their *properties:* color, shape, texture, hardness, and weight. Children study these as they observe, manipulate, compare, and even change the form or appearance of objects. As they compare properties and recognize the differences among similarly shaped pieces of aluminum, brass, lead, steel, pine, walnut, and acrylic, children assimilate the concept of *material.* Property comparison also leads children to the concept of *serial ordering.*

Your pupils investigate the properties of solid, liquid, and gaseous materials. Each child has many opportunities to apply what he has learned about material objects, their similarities and differences, the *changes* that may be brought about, and the need for observable *evidence* to support his conclusions.*

* Science Curriculum Improvement Study, *Sample Guide,* A Composite Teacher's Guide. (Chicago: Rand McNally and Company, 1970), p. 10.

In *Organisms:*

Children become familiar with some of the requirements for life as they set out seeds and watch the growth of plants. This experience is extended when the class builds aquaria with water plants, fish, and snails. Three natural events occurring in the aquaria are observed and discussed: *birth* of guppies and appearance of snail eggs, *growth* of guppies and snails, and *death* of organisms.

When they explore the school yard, nearby park, or nature area, children discover plants and animals living outside the classroom. Children are led to the concept of *habitat* as they compare these land organisms with those living in the aquaria.

After a few weeks, the algae in some of the aquaria increase in sufficient numbers to make the water green. The children usually notice this change and sometimes ask about its cause. Through a series of experiments and observations they recognize the presence of tiny green plants called algae. Children may then find evidence that algae are eaten by *Daphnia* (water fleas). When they discover that guppies feed upon *Daphnia,* the children can use this series of observations as the basis for understanding the concept of a *food web* depicting feeding relationships among organisms.

Detritus, the black material accumulating on the sand in aquaria after a few weeks, is a combination of feces and dead plants and animals. Children infer, as they compare seeds grown in sand with and without detritus, that it acts as a fertilizer, enhancing plant growth.

Each experience with living organisms should increase the child's awareness of differences between living organisms and nonliving objects.*

The two units suggested for second grade are *Interaction* and *Life Cycles.* In the *Interaction* unit,

---

* Science Curriculum Improvement Study, *Sample Guide,* A Composite Teacher's Guide. (Chicago: Rand McNally and Company, 1970), p. 10.

The central concept of the entire SCIS program, *interaction,* is introduced in this unit. The children's work with objects and organisms in the first year has given the background necessary for understanding the interaction relationship. In later units, the program will emphasize the application and refinement of the interaction concept as children investigate biological, chemical, electrical, magnetic, thermal, and mechanical phenomena.

The first two parts of this unit are devoted to the interaction and systems concepts, respectively. The idea that a change may often be interpreted as evidence of interaction (for example, when photographic paper turns dark on exposure to sunlight) is explained. The remainder of the unit is divided into four parts in which (children) investigate interactions and systems: pulley systems, dissolving (copper chloride, aluminum), interaction-at-a-distance (interaction without the objects touching, as in magnetism), and electric circuits. You may alter the sequence of these investigations to suit your preference. Throughout, children observe and interpret evidence of interaction.

Scientific concepts are developed in the unit, as are the children's skills in (1) manipulating experimental equipment, (2) reporting observations, and (3) recording observations during experiments.*

In the unit *Life Cycles,*

The investigation of ecosystems begun in *Organisms* is continued in *Life Cycles.* The unit, however, focuses on individual organisms, which alone show the characteristics of the phenomenon we call "life." At this time the interrelationships and interdependencies within the ecosystem have secondary importance.

Each kind of plant and animal has its own life cycle. By studying the life cycles of selected plants and animals, children observe the characteristics of living organisms. Seeds

* Science Curriculum Improvement Study, *Sample Guide,* A Composite Teacher's Guide. (Chicago: Rand McNally and Company, 1970), p. 11.

are planted and their germination observed. Plants are cared for until they reach maturity, produce flowers, and form a new generation of seeds. The fruit fly, frog, and mealworm are observed while they metamorphose (change body form). As one generation of organisms produces another, children are led to consider biotic potential and the effects of reproduction and death on a population. Finally, when some of the similarities and differences between plants and animals have been considered, and children have defined the two categories on the basis of their own observations they proceed to the more general question, "What is alive?" With each experience, a child's awareness of the differences between living and nonliving objects should increase.*

There are two physical science units and one life science unit which have been developed for the third grade. The physical science units are *Subsystems* and *Variables*.

The subsystems concept is introduced to give the children a grouping of objects intermediate between a single object and an entire system. The grains of sand in a mixture of sand, salt, and baking soda, the salt in a salt solution, the Freon in a bag interacting with water, or the arm and rivets in a whirlybird system are all examples of subsystems.

As the children experiment with solid and liquid materials they use the techniques of sifting to separate solid powders and of filtering to separate an undissolved solid from a liquid. At the same time they recognize that dissolved solids in *solutions* cannot be separated by filtering. Instead, the presence of dissolved solids may be identified by *schlieren* or by a residue that remains after the liquid evaporates. There are further experiences with the liquid Freon, a material that not only evaporates quickly at room temperature but that condenses to a liquid form when cooled with ice. The work with solutions and with Freon serve to deepen the children's awareness of the principle of conservation of matter, even

* Science Curriculum Improvement Study, *Sample Guide,* A Composite Teacher's Guide. (Chicago: Rand McNally and Company, 1970), p. 11.

though this is not stated explicitly in the unit. The technique of using a histogram to compare data is introduced when the children take temperature readings during the melting of ice and interpret their measurements.

In the last part of this unit, children investigate the whirlybird and discover that its operation depends on many factors they can control and on a few they cannot. The *variable* concept helps them to identify and investigate factors influencing the motion of the whirlybird arm.*

The life science unit for the third grade is *Population*.

In this unit attention is directed toward populations of organisms rather than toward individual plants and animals.

Children observe the growth, eventual leveling off, and decline of isolated populations of *Daphnia*, aphids, and fruit flies. They relate increased population sizes to reproduction and population decline to death.

The children build aquaria and terraria in which several populations live together. The aquaria contain populations of *Daphnia*, hydra, snails, algae, duckweed, and *Anacharis*. The terraria contain grass, clover, crickets, and chameleons. By observing the interacting populations in the aquaria and terraria, the children gain some understanding of the relationships among populations in nature. For example, the children observe that hydra eat *Daphnia*, with the result that the *Daphnia* population declines while the hydra population may increase. In the terraria, the children observe that crickets eat grass and clover and that when chameleons are added to the terraria they eat the crickets. Thus, the grass and clover populations are reduced, and the cricket population is eventually wiped out.*

As in the third grade, there are two units suggested for the fourth grade, one in physical science—*Relative Position and Motion*—and one in life science—*Environments*.

* Science Curriculum Improvement Study, *Sample Guide*, Composite Teacher's Guide. (Chicago: Rand McNally and Company, 1970), p. 12.

In the *Relative Position and Motion* unit, activities dealing specifically with spatial relationships are introduced into the SCIS program. The investigations enhance the children's abilities to think critically, interpret evidence, and work independently. These are process objectives for the entire SCIS program. Children use *reference frames* to describe the position and motion of objects in their everyday environment.

Early in the unit, the artificial observer Mr. O serves the children as a *reference object* for describing relative position. Later they are introduced to *polar* and *rectangular coordinates* for a more exact description of *relative position and motion*. The children must apply the reference–frame concept in many activities, such as the following: (1) playing classroom games to locate objects, and solving puzzles that require matching of relative positions; (2) watching the *Fun House* film loop in which the camera rides along with the children to record unusual relative motion; (3) drawing and interpreting flip books; and (4) orienting themselves in Yellowstone National Park with the help of maps and coordinate grids, and surveying the school playground with a simple transit. The investigations in the last part, dealing with the motion and tracks of rolling and interacting steel balls, relate the ideas and techniques developed in early parts of this unit to the matter, interaction, and energy concepts of the physical–science sequence.*

In the unit *Environments,*

The terraria children design and build at the beginning of the unit reflect their preconceptions regarding the needs of organisms. As a result, there is a wide disparity in the growth and survival of the organisms living in the terraria, and these differences can be correlated with variations in *environmental factors* such as temperature, amount of water, and intensity of light. The term *environment* is defined as

* Science Curriculum Improvement Study, *Sample Guide,* Composite Teacher's Guide. (Chicago: Rand McNally and Company, 1970), p. 13.

the sum total of all the environmental factors affecting an organism.

Afterwards, the children seek to determine the responses of individual kinds of animals and plants to variations in the environmental factors. On the basis of experiments with iso-pods in a runway with graded temperature, the concepts of a temperature *range* and of an *optimum range* for that animal are introduced. In additional experiments, (children) attempt to determine optimum ranges of other environmental factors for snails, mealworms, beans, grass, and clover. Before the unit is concluded, the children again construct terraria, but now they use their data on optimum ranges to plant a more favorable environment for their organisms.*

The units presently developed for the fifth grade are *Energy Sources* and *Communities*.

Children continue their study of matter and energy in the *Energy Sources* unit and also extend their skills in conduct-ing scientific investigations. Their attention is focused on the energy transformations that accompany the interaction of matter in solid, liquid, and gaseous forms. The children's qualitative descriptions of energy transfer from a source to a receiver prepare them for later quantitative investigations of energy exchange.

The introductory investigations employing rolling spheres and paper airplanes are used to review interaction, vari-ables, and other concepts with which the children have become familiar. These experiences and work with roto-planes (propeller-driven rotating platforms) provide back-ground for the invention of energy transfer and the identifi-cation of *energy sources* and *energy receivers*.

(Children) apply the new concepts to situations in which motion or temperature change provide evidence of energy transfer. They experiment with (1) stopper poppers, in

* Science Curriculum Improvement Study, *Sample Guide,* Composite Teacher's Guide. (Chicago: Rand McNally and Company, 1970), p. 13.

which compressed air serves as energy source; (2) spheres rolling down ramps and colliding with a movable target, in which the rolling spheres serve as energy source; (3) the dissolving of solid sodium thiosulfate or magnesium sulfate, in which the water or the solid material acts as energy source; and (4) the melting of ice, in whch the ice serves as energy receiver.

In the *Communities* unit (children) investigate the food relations within a *community* of plants and animals. They experiment with germinating plants, discovering that food stored in cotyledons is consumed; however, another source of food, photosynthesis, supports the plants' growth.

The children observe the feeding behavior of animals in terraria containing various plants and animals. They identify the food chains and infer that photosynthesis in green plants not only supplies food for the plants but indirectly also for the animals in the community. The children count the large number of wheat seeds eaten by crickets and the few crickets eaten by a single frog. On the basis of these data, the *food* pyramid is introduced.

When an animal or plant in the terrarium dies without being eaten by another animal, the children place the dead organism in a vial and cover it with moist soil. They observe the organism's gradual decomposition along with the appearance of mold or an unpleasant odor. The children are told that organisms that satisfy their energy needs by decomposing the bodies of dead plants and animals are bacteria and molds.

The transfer of food through a community is illustrated by means of a chart showing the food relations among plants, animals, bacteria, and molds. The plants are identified as *producers,* the animals as *consumers,* and the molds and bacteria as *decomposers*. The interacting producers, consumers, and decomposers in a given area constitute the community.*

* Science Curriculum Improvement Study, *Sample Guide,* Composite Teacher's Guide. (Chicago: Rand McNally and Company), 1970, p. 14.

The basic objective of the units for the sixth grade, *Models: Electric and Magnetic Interactions* and *Ecosystems,* is for the student to develop an understanding of working models.

Through the investigations in the Ecosystems unit, children become aware of the roles played by oxygen, carbon dioxide, and water in the maintenance of life. When this understanding is combined with the habitat, populations, community, and other concepts introduced in the SCIS life-science sequence, the term *ecosystem* acquires its full meaning.

Initially, (children) review the ideas introduced in the five earlier units by building a composite terrarium—aquarium. The organisms living in the containers represent plants, plant eaters, and animal eaters—organisms that flourish under varying environmental conditions. The *ecosystem* is defined as the system composed of a community of organisms interacting with its environment.

After they observe water droplets on the inside of the terraria—aquaria, the children clarify the role of water in an ecosystem. The *water cycle* refers to the succession of evaporation and condensation of water.

(Children) study the carbon dioxide—oxygen exchange between organisms and their environment. They test their own preconceptions about oxygen and carbon dioxide when they compare the gases formed by plants exposed to light and to the dark, by animals, living in a community with plants, and by animals in isolation. The production and consumption of the two gases is described as the *carbon dioxide—oxygen cycle*.

The activities in the *Models* unit are directed toward increasing the children's understanding of electrical and magnetic phenomena at the levels of concrete experiences and of abstract thought.

Children review some of their work in the Interaction and Systems and Subsystems and Variables units. Next, children explore the circuits' energy sources, constructing a battery (or *electrochemical cell*) to operate light bulbs and other circuit elements. Finally, the model concept is introduced in connection with mechanical and electrical "mystery systems." (Children) must explain the systems in terms of assumed objects that cannot be seen directly.

The second part of the unit is devoted to magnetism and various models, such as the magnetic field and the magnetic poles. In Part Three (children) investigate more complicated electric circuits, and the *electric current* model is introduced to unify their theories. The distinction between *series* and *parallel* electric-circuit connections can be used for predicting the operation of light bulbs and other circuit elements if a consistent model for electric current has been chosen.

In the concluding activities, electric energy sources and the chemical processes related to electric current flow are considered again.*

For each unit, there is a Teacher's Guide and student activity sheets or a student manual. Common elements of the Teacher's Guide include:

1. Title
2. Conceptual Framework
3. Program Overview
4. Clues for the Teachers
5. Design and Use of the Kit
6. Instructional Activities (including Objectives and Teaching Suggestions)
7. Glossary of Important Terms

The section dealing with *Organisms* illustrates the seven parts that make up the unit.

1. Title

Organisms describes the general area on which the student experiences will be focused.

* Science Curriculum Improvement Study, *Sample Guide,* Composite Teacher's Guide. (Chicago: Rand McNally and Company), 1970, p. 15.

2. Conceptual Framework *

Change and diversity, in the weather and at the zoo, or elsewhere, always arouse our interest and attract attention. Children, curious about their surroundings, naturally seek to organize and catalog the diversity of animals, plants, and nonliving materials they discover. In this respect, they resemble scientists, who are devoted to understanding the basic conditions governing change. Through investigation, scientists advance the frontiers of knowledge. Similarly, children advance their thinking processes from the concrete to the abstract and develop a disciplined curiosity as they accumulate experiences and ideas. In other words, they become scientifically literate.

A person's scientific literacy results from his basic knowledge, investigative experience, and curiosity. In the SCIS program, these three factors are integrated, balanced, and developed through the children's involvement with major scientific concepts, key process-oriented concepts, and challenging problems for investigation.

Content, Process, and Attitude

Educators frequently distinguish among content, process, and attitude when they describe an educational program or evaluate its outcomes. The SCIS program combines these factors. Children are introduced to knowledge of scientific content through their experiences with diverse physical and biological materials. And, in the course of their investigations, they engage in observation, measurement, interpretation, prediction, and other processes.

The SCIS program helps children form positive attitudes toward science as they explore phenomena according to their own preconceptions. They learn to cope confidently with new and unexpected findings by sifting evidence and forming conclusions.

* Science Curriculum Improvement Study, *Organisms, Teacher's Guide.* (Chicago: Rand McNally and Company, 1970), pp. 8–11.

Interaction

Central to modern science, and therefore also to the SCIS program, is the view that changes take place because objects interact in reproducible ways under similar conditions. Changes do not occur because they are preordained or because a "spirit" or other power within objects influences them capriciously. By *interaction* we refer to the relation among objects or organisms that do something to one another, thereby bringing about a change. For instance, when a magnet picks up a steel pin, we say that the magnet and the pin interact. The observed change itself, the pin jumping toward the magnet, is evidence of interaction. Children can easily observe and use such evidence. As they advance from a dependence on concrete experiences to the ability to think abstractly, children identify the conditions under which interaction occurs and predict its outcome.

Major Scientific Concepts

The four major scientific concepts we use to elaborate the interaction viewpoint are matter, energy, organism, and ecosystem. Children's experiences and investigations in the physical–science sequence are based on the first two; the last two provide the framework of the life–science sequence. Additional concepts are described in the appropriate teacher's guides.

Matter, perceived as the solid objects, liquids, and gases in the environment, is tangible. It interacts with human sense organs, and pieces of matter interact with each other. Material objects may be described and recognized by their color, shape, weight, texture, and other properties. As children investigate changes in objects during their work in the SCIS physical-science program, they become aware of the diversity of interacting objects and of their properties.

The second major concept is *energy,* the inherent ability of an animal, a flashlight battery, or other system to bring about changes in the state of its surroundings or in itself. Some familiar sources of energy are the burning gas used to heat a kettle of water, the unwinding spring that operates a watch, and the discharging battery in a pocket radio. The counterpart of an energy source is an energy receiver, and a very important natural process is the interaction between source and receiver that results in energy transfer.

The third concept is that of a living *organism*. An organism is an entire living individual, plant or animal. It is composed of matter and can use the energy imparted by its food to build its body and be active. The organism concept therefore represents a fusion of the matter and energy concepts, but it is also broader than these, so we identify and describe it separately.

As children observe living plants and animals in the classroom or outdoors, they become aware of the amazing diversity of organisms and their life cycles. They observe how plants and animals interact with one another and with the soil, atmosphere, and sun in the vast network of relations that constitute life. The focus of the SCIS life-science program is the organism-environment relationship.

The study of life focused on organism-environment interaction leads to the *ecosystem* concept. Thinking about a forest may help you understand the ecosystem. A forest is more than an assemblage of trees. Living in the shade of the trees are shrubs, vines, herbs, ferns, mosses, and toadstools. In addition the forest swarms with insects, birds, mammals, reptiles, and amphibians. A forest is all of these plants and animals living together. The animals depend on the plants for food and living conditions. The plants use sunlight, carbon dioxide, water, and minerals to make food to sustain themselves and other organisms in the forest. The interrelated plants, animals, sun, air, water, and soil constitute an ecosystem.

Process-oriented Concepts

In addition to the scientific concepts described above, four process-oriented concepts are also extremely important. They are *property, reference frame, system,* and *model.* These concepts, together with others that relate to specific units, are at the heart of the processes of observing, describing, comparing, classifying, measuring, interpreting evidence, and experimenting.

We have already referred to the *properties* by which an object may be described or recognized. A property is any quality that enables you to compare objects. Properties also enable you to describe or compare concepts. For example, place value is a property of digits in the decimal number system; the term climate (hot, cold, temperate) summarizes the properties of weather in a specific region; and food production is a property of green plants.

Every description and comparison of natural or social phenomena reflects the observer's point of view or frame of reference. For the young child, who relates objects to himself rather than to other things, the discovery of other frames of reference is a challenge.

In science, where the position (location) and motion of objects are important subjects of study, the *reference–frame* idea has been developed into the awesome relativity theory. Yet the basic concept, as included in the SCIS program, is simple: the position and motion of objects can be perceived, described, and recognized only with reference to other objects. When you say, "The car is at the south end of the parking lot," you describe the location of the car relative to the parking lot. In this example, the parking lot and compass direction serve as a reference frame. However, when you say, "The car is to your left," the listener's body serves as a reference frame. A child who considers several reference frames thereby overcomes the usual self-centered viewpoint.

The third process-oriented concept is that of a *system,* which SCIS defines as a group of related objects that make up a whole. It may include the battery and circuits that make up an operating pocket radio, or it may consist of a seed and the moist soil in which it is planted. The system concept stems from the realization that objects or organisms do not function in isolation, but exist in a context while interacting with other objects or organisms.

A subsystem is part of another system. Thus, moist soil is it-self a system comprised of clay, sand, water, and decayed matter. It is at the same time a subsystem of the seed–moist soil system. The seed, with its coat, embryo, and stored food, is another sub-system.

Sometimes it is hard to decide what to include when defining a system: Does the soil–seed system include the air that permeates the soil? Ordinarily children would not include air since moisture is usually the most important factor in germination. However, if a child were to deprive the soil–seed system of air, the result would make him aware of its importance to plant growth.

A system becomes a new system whenever matter is added to or removed from it. When nothing is added or removed a system retains its identity, even though it may change in form or appear-ance. When selecting a system, children focus their attention, or-ganize their observations, and relate the whole system to its parts (objects or subsystems). They become skillful in tracing a system through a sequence of changes.

The fourth process-oriented concept, the scientific *model*, may be illustrated by the example of an automatic vending machine that dispenses candy. You insert a dime into a slot, push one of several buttons, and out falls a particular candy bar. You could imagine that the dime unlocks the buttons and that a button pushes your candy off its shelf and down the chute. Such an imag-ined system would be a model. A scientific model is a mental image of a real system to which you assign certain parts or prop-erties that you cannot see directly. The successful model provides a possible explanation of how the system functions, but it may not give an accurate description of what really happens in the system. Usually the model is simpler than the real system it represents.

Scientific models permit children to relate their present obser-vations to their previous experiences with similar systems. Models satisfy the children's need for thinking in concrete terms. Models also lead to predictions and new discoveries about the system being investigated. You may, for instance, make predictions and test your candy–machine model by pushing a different button or by pushing two buttons at once.

SCIS PROGRAM

PHYSICAL SCIENCE	LIFE SCIENCE
Material Objects	Organisms
Interaction and Systems	Life Cycles
Subsystems and Variables	Populations
Relative Position and Motion	Environments
Energy Sources	Communities
Models: Electric and Magnetic Interactions	Ecosystems

Physical-Science Sequence

The unity of the SCIS physical–science sequence comes from the fundamental concepts of change and interaction. The six basic units, *Material Objects, Interaction and Systems, Subsystems and Variables, Relative Position and Motion, Energy Sources,* and *Models: Electric and Magnetic Interactions,* introduce and develop the scientific and process-oriented concepts necessary for scientific literacy.

Life-Science Sequence

The units in the life–science sequence pay continuing attention to organism–environment interactions. The six basic units, *Organ-*

isms, Life Cycles, Populations, Environments, Communities, and *Ecosystems,* make use of the scientific and process-oriented concepts but add the special considerations appropriate to the study of life. The *Ecosystems* unit achieves a synthesis of the children's investigations in physical and life science.

Optional Units

The entire SCIS program is not a neatly wrapped package but rather a beginning—a foundation for exploration of many fascinating happenings. Optional units are being planned to extend the basic sequences in physical and life science.

3. Program Overview *

In this section, a brief overview of the ideas and experiences in the unit are summarized.

The First Year

The first-year units are *Material Objects* and *Organisms.* These units have certain common objectives: to sharpen children's powers of observation, discrimination, and accurate description. The objectives are accomplished as children care for aquatic plants and animals, raise seedlings, and investigate the properties of a broad range of nonliving solid specimens (metal, wood, plastic, sand, ice), liquids (water, oil), and gases (air, Freon). The units complement each other and can be taught effectively in either order.

Material Objects

Common objects and special materials provided in the kit are described by their *properties:* color, shape, texture, hardness, and weight. Children study these as they observe, manipulate, com-

---

* Science Curriculum Improvement Study, *Organisms, Teacher's Guide.* (Chicago: Rand McNally and Company, 1970), pp. 12–13.

pare, and even change the form or appearance of objects. As they compare properties and recognize the differences among similarly shaped pieces of aluminum, brass, lead, steel, pine, walnut, and acrylic, children assimilate the concept of *material*. Property comparison also leads children to the concept of *serial ordering*.

In the last part of this unit, the children continue to investigate the properties of solid, liquid, and gaseous materials. Thus, each child has many opportunities to apply what he has learned about material objects, their similarities and differences, the *changes* that may be brought about, and the need for observable *evidence* to support his conclusions. This work also sets the stage for his studies in *Interaction and Systems,* where he relates the properties of objects to their ability to interact.

Provision has been made in the student manual for children to record their observations or inferences. Children are thus encouraged to relate their actual experiences to their use of the printed page, an ability which is an essential part of reading with understanding. All the activities stimulate language development because each child acquires experiences about which he is eager to talk. At the same time, these concepts basic to the science program are introduced and used repeatedly:

object	serial ordering
property	change
material	evidence

Organisms

Children become familiar with some of the requirements for life as they set out seeds and watch the growth of plants. This experience is extended when the class builds aquaria with water plants, fish, and snails. Three natural events occurring in the aquaria are observed and discussed: *birth* of guppies and appearance of snail eggs; *growth* of guppies and snails; and *death* of organisms.

When they explore the school yard, nearby park, or nature area, children discover plants and animals living outside the classroom. Your students are led to the concept of *habitat* as they compare these land organisms with those living in the aquaria.

After a few weeks, the algae in some of the aquaria increase in sufficient numbers to make the water green. The children usually notice this change and sometimes ask about its cause. Through a series of experiments and observations they recognize the presence of tiny green plants called algae. Children may then find evidence that algae are eaten by *Daphnia* (water fleas). When they discover that guppies feed upon *Daphnia,* the children can use this series of observations as the basis for understanding the concept of a *food web* depicting feeding relationships among organisms.

Detritus, the black material accumulating on the sand in aquaria after a few weeks, is a combination of feces and dead plants and animals. Children infer, as they compare seeds grown in sand with and without detritus, that it functions as a fertilizer, enhancing plant growth. With this final activity, illustrating the interrelatedness of organisms and their environment, class attention is returned to the plants observed at the beginning of the unit.

Each experience with living organisms should increase the child's awareness of the differences between living organisms and nonliving objects. At the same time, he will develop some understanding of a few fundamental biological concepts:

organism	habitat
birth	food web
death	detritus

4. Clues to the Teacher*

This section contains many helpful hints to the teacher about the organization of the guide, the sequence of parts of the unit, the use of exploration lessons, invention activities, and discovery experiences, the role of the teacher in the classroom, discussion, and

* Science Curriculum Improvement Study, *Organisms, Teacher's Guide.* (Chicago: Rand McNally and Company, 1970), pp. 14–16.

evaluation. The use of reference books, and the relationship of this unit to previous units, are included.

As you plan your science classes keep in mind that the SCIS teaching program is not organized into tightly structured lessons. Rather, a unit is composed of several parts, each part having specific objectives. The parts, in turn, are divided into chapters. Each chapter may contain several activities.

A certain rationale underlies each part. You will find it explained in the section titled "Background Information." The individual chapters contain suggestions for scheduling the activities. There is no student manual for this unit.

One activity may extend beyond a single class period, or several may be included in one session. While most of the activities are intended to be carried out by small groups, other activities will be more successful when the whole class works together.

Your willingness to improvise and to depart from your lesson plans will better enable you to meet your pupils' needs. Sometimes students ask questions that do not lead in the direction you planned. If that happens permit yourself and the class the pleasure of a side trip that may lead to fruitful experiences. In addition, encourage pupils to explore some of their questions independently.

The Learning Cycle

The SCIS program provides for three stages in the learning cycle of children. These stages, which we term exploration, invention, and discovery, are explained more fully below. They are based on current theories of how children learn.

Exploration

Children learn through their own spontaneous behavior relative to objects and events. From the beginning of the unit, therefore, children have direct contact with plants and animals. The exploratory activities provide initial direct contact with organisms, in a situation that permits children to make their own, if somewhat limited, discoveries.

Invention

Spontaneous learning is limited by the child's preconceptions. After exploration, he needs new concepts to interpret his observations. Since few children can phrase new concepts by themselves, you must at times provide a definition and a term for a new concept. This constitutes the "invention." Be clear and explicit when you give a definition, repeating it several times if necessary. To give the children opportunities to use the new concept, encourage them to look for examples that illustrate the new idea. When they report such examples immediately or during later discovery activities, you gain feedback about their understanding of the concept. The conclusion of an invention lesson may turn into a free-ranging discussion of the validity of these examples.

Discovery

We use the word *discovery* for those activities in which a child discerns a new application for a concept. You may plan a variety of situations leading to discovery or you may depend on a child's own experiences to furnish these applications. The children's discovery activities reinforce the original concept and enlarge and refine its meaning. In this way mastery and retention of concepts are aided by practice and repeated, wide application.

Discovery is most effective when there is considerable variety in the examples investigated so that repetition occurs with respect to the concept illustrated.

Implementing the Learning Cycle

The three stages of exploration, invention, and discovery apply to the science concepts introduced in this unit. For example, the children explore the area around the school yard looking for organisms and where they live. On the basis of this experience the concept "habitat" is introduced and defined. After this the children discover other examples of habitats in the aquaria, outside the school, and in books.

Discussions

Conversation among children or between teacher and children is an important part of the learning process. While participating in individual or group experiments, children spontaneously exchange observations and ideas with one another. During an invention session, the teacher illustrates and explains a new concept. When gathering feedback, the teacher may address a specific question to a particular child.

On other occasions, we suggest discussions in which the children report on their experimental results, compare observations, and sometimes challenge one another's findings. Many children should participate in these discussions; and you, the teacher, should avoid controlling the topic or the pace. Encourage the children to comment to each other without specifically calling them to recite in turn. Grouping them to face inward around an open area promotes their speaking to one another. If you call attention to disagreement between two findings, you invite evaluative comments and suggestions from the class.

Asking Questions

The questions you ask and the way you ask them will affect the children's work and attitudes. Note the difference between "What did we study yesterday?" and "What did you find out yesterday?" Both questions call for a review of a previous activity, but the former seeks an answer already in the teacher's mind, while the latter inquires into a child's own experience.

Questions that aim for a predetermined answer are often called *convergent* because of their specific goals. Most questions in multiple-choice tests are of this nature, as are many questions asked by classroom teachers. Questions that allow a variety of answers are often called *divergent* because they may lead in many directions. Provocative discussion questions are usually of this nature.

Adjust your questions to your purpose in asking them. If you wish to spark discussion, ask a divergent question and then sit back while several children propose answers. Examples of such questions are "What made the water in the aquaria green?" or "Where did the black stuff on the sand come from?" You achieve one of your objectives if children continue the discussion with one another without your leadership.

If you wish to gather feedback about a particular child's understanding or recalling of a certain fact, ask him a convergent question. This may be done individually or in a small group. Two examples are "What are two properties of a pumpkin seed?" or "Which guppies are male and which are female?"

Feedback

Feedback is information that comes to a person in response to something that person did. As a teacher, you are collecting feedback from your pupils most of the time. An answer to a question yields feedback. So does a child who looks out the window during your demonstration. In this guide we have tried to alert you to feedback situations in which your pupils' responses are likely to influence your teaching plans.

Language Development

During extensive use in urban, rural, and suburban schools, the earlier editions of *Organisms* proved to be particularly helpful as part of the overall effort to improve children's oral language skills. The experience with real and interesting materials was especially effective in the case of disadvantaged or deprived children whose desire to speak and participate in class discussion increased dramatically.

Optional Activities

To make the teaching program flexible, optional activities have been included in most chapters. These make use of the equipment listed for the main activities or require you to supply readily available items such as rulers, construction paper, and containers of various kinds, such as milk cartons. As you plan a science period, you may use the optional activities in any one of several ways:

1. They may be integrated into the main activities if a child raises a related question.

2. They may be used to provide additional discovery situations for individual pupils who complete their assignments early or for pupils who show a special interest.

3. They may be used for investigation by the whole class, if you would like to emphasize one topic for which you have a preference.

4. They may be used quite extensively if the *Organisms* unit is taught to a class older than the six- or seven-year-olds for whom it is principally designed.

5. They may be used to relate the science program to math, social studies, and language arts.

We hope that you will include at least a few of the optional activities in your program, but we do not expect you to use all of them.

Reference Material

Children will raise many questions during the course of this unit, and some will immediately want to look for answers in books. Encourage them, instead, to turn to the living systems in the classroom so that they learn to obtain firsthand evidence instead of relying on statements made by others. Books, however, can be used in this program. During discovery activities, children should use opportunities to search in books for applications of a particular concept.

5. Design and Use of the Kit*

This list describes both the equipment supplied and where it is to be found in the materials. Those items to be shipped from the publisher's warehouse are also identified. The kit has been designed to simplify and make convenient the use, storage, and re-use of the required equipment and supplies. The necessary materials are listed at the beginning of each chapter. Standard classroom supplies, such as crayons and scissors, must be furnished by the teacher. The freshwater organisms with which the aquaria are to be stocked are not sent with the kit. Instead they will be sent separately upon the supplier's receipt of the appropriate order form. Please mail Form A or B three weeks before the date on which you wish to receive that group of organisms.

Since practically all the activities require living plants and animals, it is best to teach *Organisms* in the fall and in the spring. In most parts of the United States it is very difficult to successfully transport living organisms in the middle of winter and to keep them alive in your classroom if the temperature there remains below 60°F for any length of time.

DRAWER	ITEM DESCRIPTION AND QUANTITY
1 Planter Materials	36 planter cups
	36 planter bases
	2 light sources
	4 packages seeds
	3 water sprinklers
	16 paper plates
	1 roll labels
2 Aquaria	6 one-gallon plastic containers
3 Aquaria	6 one-gallon plastic containers
4 Aquaria	6 one-gallon plastic containers

* Science Curriculum Improvement Study, *Organisms, Teacher's Guide*. (Chicago: Rand McNally and Company, 1970), p. 17.

5	Aquaria Materials	1 bottle plant nutrient 2 dip nets (coarse and fine) 32 plastic tumblers 16 magnifiers 1 package fish food 2 living–material order forms (A and B) 16 medicine droppers
6	Filtering Materials	1 baster 1 roll labels 16 plastic funnels 1 package cotton balls
7	Small Containers	70 plastic bags 70 "twistems" 16 plastic tumblers 22 vials

Sand and Soil Box:

- 1 bag soil (12 lb)
- 2 bags white sand (16 lb/bag)

Shipment A:

- 10 male guppies
- 26 female guppies
- 18 pond snails
- 12 sprigs *Anacharis*
- 12 sprigs eelgrass
- 1 jar duckweed
- 1 jar *Chlamydomonas*

Shipment B:

- 3 jars *Daphnia* culture

6. Instructional Activities*

The introduction provides an overview for the first group of chapters which identifies the interrelationships between these chapters. Instructional objectives may be found in the introduction or within individual chapters.

OBSERVING AND PLANTING SEEDS

The children observe four kinds of seeds. They plant the seeds in soil-filled containers.

Teaching Materials

For each team of two children:

  2 pumpkin seeds (Drawer 1)
  2 pea seeds (Drawer 1)
  4 mustard seeds (Drawer 1)
20 ryegrass seeds (Drawer 1)
  2 planter cups (Drawer 1)
  2 planter bases (Drawer 1)
  1 paper plate (Drawer 1)
  2 labels (Drawer 1)
  1 magnifier (Drawer 5)

For the class:

  4 pumpkin seeds
  4 pea seeds
  8 mustard seeds
40 ryegrass seeds
  2 planter cups

* Science Curriculum Improvement Study, *Organisms, Teacher's Guide.* (Chicago: Rand McNally and Company, 1970), pp. 22–23.

2 planter bases
2 labels
3 sprinklers (Drawer 1)
1 bag soil

Advance Preparation

Prepare sixteen paper plates, each with two pumpkin seeds, two pea, four mustard, and about twenty grass seeds. Provide three stations in the classroom for the distribution of the planters, soil, and magnifiers.

Teaching Suggestions

Observing Seeds

The children should work in pairs. Give each team a paper plate containing the seed mixture. Ask the children to observe the seeds with their magnifiers and to sort them into groups. The seeds in each group should all have the same properties.

Instruct the children to use the magnifiers properly. Tell them to hold a lens close to one eye and then to move the object back and forth until it can be seen clearly. The smallest lens gives the greatest magnification. This lens has to be held closer to the eye than the larger ones.

The children's interest should determine the extent to which they explore seed characteristics.

Planting Seeds

When the children have finished observing the seeds, one child in each team may plant pumpkin seeds and ryegrass while the other child plants peas and mustard seeds. It is important that each child plants both large and small seeds.

Each child will need a planter cup filled (not quite to the top) with soil and a base. The planter cup has holes in the bottom to permit water drainage. It fits into the base, which collects water and prevents a mess. You may prepare these in advance or let the children fix their own.

Show your class how to plant the pumpkin seeds and peas in the soil. Drop one seed into a hole about an inch deep and cover it with soil. Mustard and ryegrass seeds can be sprinkled on the surface and then covered with a thin layer of soil. The seeds should be well spaced. Each child should label his planter with his name.

Watering

After all the seeds have been planted, ask how often the cups should be watered. On the basis of the children's responses, divide the class into at least two groups—one recommending little watering, the other recommending frequent watering. If some children suggest an intermediate amount, let them form a third group.

Arrange the planters in the room according to the watering schedule—the planters to be watered frequently in one group, those to be watered less often in another. Be sure to place all planters where they will receive the most light—under either natural or artificial light. Set up schedules for all groups, reminding them when it is time to water. The children should use sprinklers so their seeds are not inundated. Devise some means for all the children to share in the responsibility.

It may be difficult to keep the children to their initial arrangements. Those who, in the beginning, decided to water their plants infrequently may change their minds and want to water every day. If this happens, let the children change their schedules, explaining their reasons.

To insure that the class will have some healthy plants to observe at the end of the experiment, you should plant two planters with seeds. Water them three times a week, more heavily on Friday and Monday.

Depth of Planting

Some child (or you) may raise the question of how deeply the seeds can be planted and still sprout. The children may experiment by planting seeds at different depths. They should use extra planters and seeds for these experiments, recording the name of the seed and depth of planting on a label. If you run out of planters, use milk cartons, aluminum muffin tins, or cupcake liners. An ample supply of seeds has been provided in the kit. We suggest that you save extra seeds for future experiments.

Optional Activities

You may wish to devise optional activities around the following questions and ideas:

1. Will a seed grow in water only?

2. How is growth affected by planting seeds in different positions, e.g., the pumpkin seed planted point down instead of point up?

3. Will a cracked or broken seed grow?

4. Will a seed grow in sand or on a wet sponge?

5. The children can look for seeds in a field or vacant lot near the school. If such a trip is not feasible, encourage the children to explore their yards at home.

6. Children may visit a local supermarket as a class or go there with parents. They will find it interesting to examine grocery shelves where spices, nut meats, dry beans, and pet foods are stocked. The produce counters should provide examples of fresh foods containing seeds. You may suggest they also search for seeds in their kitchen cupboards.

7. Any seeds, or what the children consider to be seeds, may be brought to class and planted. One seed should be taped to the outside of the planter to identify the type being investigated.

TO TEACH THE SCIS MATERIALS

To adequately prepare for the teaching of an SCIS unit, in our opinion, six specific tasks are essential:

    1. Read the manual carefully to identify the science concepts

involved. Further reading in the *SCIS Elementary Science Source-book* of related material is definitely recommended. In many of these background information sections, there are suggested activities. While it is easier to read and *not do* these activities, you will find that doing them yourself will greatly increase your understanding of the scientific ideas.

2. Analyze children's activities and construct your own outline of what your children will be doing in each activity. This will help you to visualize the sequence of ideas and activities in your classroom.

3. For each activity, identify which materials will be needed and when they will be used. Are they supplied or will you need to secure them? Do the materials need to be set out ahead of time and is any previous organization necessary?

4. Perform the children's actual activities yourself first. You will find this step essential in determining a reasonable expectation of time. If it calls for seeds to germinate, do it and see how many days it takes for the seeds to germinate in your area. If it calls for ice cubes to melt, try it and find out whether it requires one hour or two days. Your confidence in being an effective guide for children's learning will be directly related to your confidence in knowing what to expect from the situation. Omitting Step 4 can be very disastrous.

5. Study the suggestions for arranging the children and the room. Rethinking the activities may suggest a need to revise the planned room arrangement or student grouping.

6. For each of the activities, write out what you will say or do to begin the activity. In a few cases, questions are included in the section "teaching suggestions." Most of the time, however, you will have to construct your own plan for involving the children.

BUT WHY SCIS?

The developers of the Science Curriculum Improvement Study specified that there ought to be, and is, a relationship between the nature of science and the program developed by SCIS. They describe this relationship as:

The present content of science consists of concepts and relationships that mankind has abstracted from the observation of natural phenomena over the centuries. This overall evolutionary process has been marked by occasional major and minor scientific revolutions which re-oriented entire fields of endeavor. Examples are the Copernican revolution in astronomy, the conception of natural selection by Darwin, and the introduction of quantum theory into atomic physics. The result is a conceptual structure and a point of view with which the scientist approaches his work.

Let us briefly consider in an overly simplified way how a scientist may proceed. From a number of similar observations the scientist formulates an hypothesis about the behavior of a class of objects in the kind of situations he has studied. He then continues to make observations in further situations to which he expects his hypothesis to apply. If the behavior always turns out to be consistent with his expectation, the hypothesis is confirmed and thereafter may be called a law of nature. If the behavior turns out to be contrary to his expectation, the hypothesis in its original form must be abandoned. . . .*

Science is, therefore, never complete. There are always some unanswered questions, some unexpected phenomena. These may eventually be resolved within the accepted structure of science, or they may force a revision of the fundamental point of view from which the phenomena were interpreted. Progress in science comes from the discovery of new phenomena and from the invention of novel interpretations that illuminate in a new way the new and the well-known phenomena. Scientific truth is, therefore, not absolute and permanent; rather, it is in accordance with the facts as currently known. Without this qualification, the statement that scientists seek the truth is misleading. It is better to say that scientists seek understanding. . . .**

* Karplus and Thier, *A New Look at Elementary School Science.* (Chicago: Rand McNally and Company, 1967), p. 25.
** Karplus and Thier, *A New Look at Elementary School Science.* (Chicago: Rand McNally and Company, 1967), p. 26.

In the previous discussion of the nature of science, reference has been made to scientific concepts and to a structure of science. It is now necessary to elaborate on the significance of these terms. One way to approach this problem is to inquire how a scientist gives meaning to a concept in such a way that its relevance to the study of natural phenomena is assured. The use of a system of dictionary definitions is clearly inadequate, for a dictionary always gives the meaning of one word in terms of other words. Ultimately, therefore, as one pursues the definitions of the definitions, the dictionary will exhaust the language. It must either include some undefined terms or its definitions must become circular. In ordinary usage this limitation of the dictionary presents no serious difficulty because its users have a fund of understanding which makes it unnecessary for them to puruse the definitions of definitions indefinitely. The dictionary is helpful because it serves to explain the unknown in terms of the known. This kind of common knowledge of a culture enables its literate members to use language for communication about concrete and abstract matters.

In a way, the scientific community may be considered a culture within which communication is possible because its members are "scientifically literate" and share a point of view or fund of common understanding. Special attention has to be devoted to the fund of common understanding, however, because it occasionally becomes an obstacle to progress and must be revised. Scientists, therefore, have developed the technique of operational definitions to specify the meaning of many terms in such a way that their connection with physical reality becomes part of the definition. Put in another way, words may be defined by other words, but they may also be defined by appeal to physical operations with concrete objects. These physical operations and concrete objects, then, are demonstrated and are not defined by mere words. . . .*

We now turn to consider the implications of the preceding remarks for the science curriculum. The teaching objec-

* Karplus and Thier, *A New Look at Elementary School Science*. (Chicago: Rand McNally and Company, 1967), pp. 27–28.

tive is to give the students sufficient knowledge and experience so that they will be able to have some understanding of scientific work being carried out by others, even though they themselves do not become scientists. This quality we have called scientific literacy. It is clear that the student can become acquainted with the experience of wrestling with a scientific problem only by carrying out investigations himself. To carry out such an investigation, however, the student must have an adequate background so that he can sense the existence of a scientific problem and can construct a tentative approach to its solution. This means he must be able to look at the potential problem situation from the "scientific point of view." *

In one issue of their *Newsletter,* the idea of scientific literacy is further specified.

When describing elementary science curricula through approaches, content process and attitude are often considered separately. Content implies emphasis on scientific concepts or theories; process, the skills to achieve such knowledge; and attitude, the development of a free and positive approach toward science and one's ability to act in scientific matters. Because SCIS sees its goal as the development of scientific literacy, no single approach alone seems appropriate. Scientific literacy is a blend of knowledge, skills, and attitudes. Thus, a curriculum aimed at such a goal must integrate these three orientations within its conceptual framework. The scientifically literate person has an understanding of scientific concepts to help him pose plausible theories about the interactions in his environment. He has familiarity with the process to test these theories out; his attitude is one which convinces him that scientific investigation has meaning to him personally—they do to the man in the laboratory or in the Senate building. He is curious about the interactions around him and sees the application of scientific thinking to all aspects of his experience.

* Karplus and Thier, *A New Look at Elementary School Science.* (Chicago: Rand McNally and Company, 1967), p. 30.

How have we proposed to develop these traits in an elementary school child? Curiosity appears to come naturally and inseparably with the child in the first year of school. It may be fostered by intellectual freedom in the classroom and spurred by interesting systems to investigate. If it can be nurtured by teachers, supported and allowed to strengthen, such curiosity could serve him in all learning situations. It is as much a job for a curriculum to keep this interest alive as it is to provide scientific materials for study.

Should intellectual freedom be the only component of a curriculum, however, the child might simply group interesting objects, watch the interactions take place, and go on to something else. He needs the opportunity to see these interactions in relation to each other, to group them under meaningful categories. The SCIS program is built around major scientific concepts that lead the child to a basic understanding of science.*

Achieving scientific literacy requires a science program that SCIS states is characterized by six principles. These principles have been identified in the SCIS *Sourcebook* as:

1. *Children need direct experiences with phenomena.* It is much better for children to handle and examine directly a snail or a magnet than to study a sketch or listen to a description. In many of the activities in the SCIS program, children have an exploratory confrontation with materials and phenomena. After concepts are introduced that help children understand the phenomena, further direct experiences are developed in which children apply these concepts in other situations. These firsthand experiences are essential if the science concepts that are introduced are to have meaning for children.

2. *Children should engage in investigations.* If children are to have some understanding of the modes of operations that

* Reprinted with permission from *SCIS Newsletter*, No. 16 (Fall 1969). Written and published by the Science Curriculum Improvement Study. Copyright 1969 by the Regents of the University of California.

are used in the sciences, they must carry out investigations themselves. To carry out such investigations, it is important that children approach problems with a sufficiently developed "scientific point of view" so that they can sense the existence of a problem and can construct a tentative approach to its solution. Early experiences in the SCIS program are designed to begin the development of this scientific point of view.

As children undertake investigations, they gain experience in the use of some of the modes of operation that are characteristic of the scientific endeavor. For example, they delineate appropriate systems and suggest hypotheses that can be used to guide their investigations. They also gain a better understanding of scientific work and continue to extend their comprehension.

3. *The child develops his own conceptual structure of science.* The child is introduced to some of the major generalizations of science that have been developed over the centuries. He has a variety of experiences in which he "discovers" how these generalizations apply in different situations. As the child is introduced to various ideas and discovers operational meanings of these statements, he develops and extends his own conceptual structure. The conceptual structure that he develops provides him with an approach to the investigation of problems in science.

4. *Guidance and discussion are an integral part of the program.* While it is an extremely important fact that children have the opportunity to explore and experiment, there should also be substantial guidance and discussion. Some of the guidance takes the form of the introduction of ideas that can help youngsters interpret observations. Through discussion, the child's experiences and the concepts are related to other experiences and to the conceptual structure of science.

5. *Science activities lead children into additional science experiences.* Science is not a closed undertaking; it has an "endless frontier." Similarly, SCIS science activities have

been planned to lead children further and deeper into the study of science. There is an emphasis on "divergent" as contrasted to "convergent" questions. It is hoped that the divergent questions will lead children to seek new relationships. There is little room in a science program for the neatly packaged lesson in which all loose strings are carefully tied together. Instead, it is to be hoped that there will be many "loose ends," and that children will be attracted into investigating some of them.

It has been said that in science instruction our aim should be to "uncover" rather than to "cover" science. A neatly packaged lesson could have been developed around falling objects—all of them heavier than air. But, much would have been missed if the behavior of lighter-than-air objects when they are released had not been considered.

6. *Scientific statements are considered to be tentative in nature.* Scientific "truth" is not absolute and permanent. The early exploration of falling objects had to be revised as a result of Galileo's experiments. Our commonsense consideration of the nature of "falling" has to be revised in order to explain the experiences of an astronaut in an earth satellite who releases a camera that does not fall to the floor of the satellite. It is conceivable that when we gain further experience with falling objects on the moon, and possibly other planets, we may have to change our concepts of the nature of "falling" again. In science, such changes are to be expected and not necessarily to be feared.

Through their science experiences, children become aware of the tentative nature of truth and the importance of adopting a questioning attitude toward statements. Just because a statement is written in a book or voiced by a noted authority does not mean that the statement is "true." It may be consistent with the facts as currently known, but it is quite likely that it will be subject to change.*

THE DEVELOPMENT OF THE SCIENCE
CURRICULUM IMPROVEMENT STUDY

The general plan for the Science Curriculum Improvement Study materials development includes the incorporation of ideas which are relevant to science and which also fit both the intellectual level of the child and teaching strategies in resonance with the approach of science. These materials have required much work from many people.

The Science Curriculum Improvement Study is developing upgraded sequential physical and life science programs for the elementary school—programs which in essence turn the classroom into a laboratory. Each unit of these programs is carefully evaluated by the SCIS staff as it progresses from early exploratory stages to the published edition. The units originate as scientists' ideas for investigations that might challenge children and that illustrate key scientific concepts. The ideas are then adapted to fit the elementary school and the resulting units are used by teachers in regular classrooms. Thus, they are tested several times in elementary schools before they are published.

Central to these elementary school programs are the current ideas of intellectual development. A child's elementary school years are a period of transition as he continues the exploration of the world he began in infancy, builds the abstractions with which he interprets the world, and develops confidence in his own ideas. Extensive laboratory experiences at this time will enable him to relate scientific concepts to the real world in a meaningful way. As he matures, the continual interplay of interpretations and observations will frequently compel him to revise his ideas about his environment.

The teaching strategy is for the child to explore selected science materials. They are encouraged to investigate, to discuss what they observe, and to ask questions. The SCIS teacher has two functions: to be an observer who listens to children and notices how well they are progressing in their investigation and to be a guide who leads the children to see the relationship of their findings to the key concept of science.*

The program was initiated in 1959. For three years prior to this, Dr. Karplus was involved with the Elementary School Science Project at the University of California. During this period he and Dr. J. Myron Atkin of the University of Illinois developed the idea of exploration–invention–discovery as a strategy for involving children in the conceptual basis of their experience. After many classroom trials of ideas later to be integrated into the program, the National Science Foundation initiated support of the program in 1962. This support continues to the present.

A number of full-time staff members are located in the University of California at Berkeley campus. In the development of a unit, the following steps have been involved to the extent that resources have permitted.

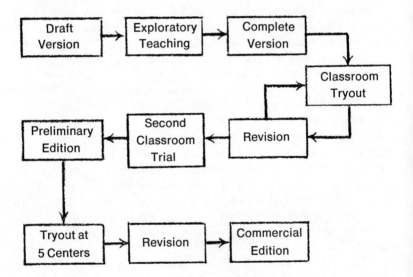

* Reprinted with permission from *SCIS Newsletter*, No. 16 (Fall 1969). Written and published by the Science Curriculum Improvement Study. Copyright 1969 by the Regents of the University of California.

As described by the SCIS staff, these steps include:

1. The SCIS staff prepares draft versions of several lessons including the design of the teaching plan, materials, and equipment based on the initial ideas suggested.

2. The draft lessons undergo exploratory teaching at several schools in the Berkeley area.

3. On the basis of the feedback from the exploratory teaching, the SCIS staff prepares a complete version of the unit including Teacher's Guide, student manuals, teaching materials, and equipment kits.

4. The SCIS staff and regular elementary school teachers conduct classroom trials of the unit in four Berkeley-area laboratory schools for one to two years.

5. The SCIS staff reconsiders the unit as a whole on the basis of first feedback from the first classroom trial on the usability of the unit and its materials. If necessary, the unit is revised and subjected to additional exploratory teaching by the SCIS staff.

6. Under the close supervision of SCIS staff, regular elementary school teachers in Berkeley then conduct second classroom trials of the unit for one or two years more.

7. The unit is again revised by the SCIS staff and a preliminary edition for commercial publication is prepared.

8. Classroom testing of the preliminary edition is again conducted in the Berkeley schools and also at the five university trial centers for two to three years more. These centers are located at Michigan State University, Columbia University, University of California at Los Angeles, University of Hawaii, and the University of Oklahoma.*

---

* "The Elementary Science Information Unit," IIU Elementary Science Curricula, Science Curriculum Improvement Study, Far West Laboratory for Educational Research and Development, Berkeley, California, 1970, p. 44.

CHAPTER 10

*Involvement Experiences
through Science —
A Process Approach*

Science—A Process Approach may be four words that are labels for experiences you have not yet had. In the episodes, you will share some of the excitement of this curriculum. These episodes are followed by a description of their sequence, a sample unit, and suggestions for teaching *Science—A Process Approach.*

Episode 10.1

A group of six-year-olds were busily engaged in finding shapes such as circles and triangles in the floor tiles, the corners of the windows, and in witches' hats. They shared in their excitement in the discovery of new instances of two-dimensional shapes in the classroom as they prepared for a "field trip" around the school building. This is their "hunt" for two- and three-dimensional shapes, shapes such as cylinders in tree limbs and rectangular prisms in the bricks of the wall. Their hunt is an extension of the week's activity in identifying shapes in both actual animals and in pictures of other animals. Precision in their description of these experiences is obvious to the casual observer.

Episode 10.2

An aquarium occupied both a prominent space in the classroom and a prominent place in the minds of members of the second-grade class. The aquarium was filled with many "interest grabbers." At almost any time during the day, one or two children could be seen observing the fish searching for food, the snails moving along the aquarium wall, or the turtle blinking from the rock float. As background for this learning experience, the children had listed all the parts of the aquarium and then had attempted to construct a classification system of this list. Their list had included water, gold fish, guppies, turtle, grass, snails, big leaf, aquarium rock, bubbler, air, and toy castle.

A first attempt at grouping these was based on plant and animal groups. However, the question of where to put things such as the water and the toy castle made the children change the grouping to "alive" and "not alive." In the first group, they included gold fish, guppies, turtle, snails. Someone then asked whether grass was alive. It was suggested that all green things are alive, when someone said that the toy castle was green and that it wasn't alive; whereas, the fish was alive but it wasn't green. The clear distinction between living and non-living was necessary before the children could proceed. Each group of four children was assigned the task of making a classification of all the parts of the aquarium so that another person could use that system. In this classroom, the children were using the information of their experience with the aquarium to develop the skill of organizing information and searching for common elements among different objects and groupings based on these common elements.

Episode 10.3

The eyes of the fourth-graders were "glued" to the center table as they watched the teacher place a jar over a lighted candle. The flame in the jar wavered slightly and then continued to burn straight and tall. It suddenly faltered, shortened, and went out, leaving only a puff of gray-white smoke. Bursting with explanations of why the candle had gone out, the children chorused ideas and comments. Listening, the teacher looked thoughtfully at the candle and jar. Finally, she asked one of the explainers how long the candle had burned under the jar. Silence. Those who were so quick to explain the event were quickly confronted with the fact that they had no idea how long the candle had burned. In each of several jars, would the candle burn the same length of time, the teacher wondered. Hunches seemed to indicate that a yes from some children was a no from others. Clearly, before they could explain this event, the children needed to know more about both the event and how to change it. In groups of three, they had the task of finding out how the candle burned in a jar. The teacher used three different size jars with the different groups so that the collective results on the board ended in sharp disagreement.

GROUP	BURNING TIME
I	14 seconds
II	6 seconds
III	19 seconds
IV	7 seconds
V	20 seconds
VI	16 seconds

Since each group "knew" it had done a *very* careful job in collecting data, the other groups must have been sloppy. The "people problem" in science results from not being careful in doing an activity. Other children noted that their jars were not the same. In fact, the jars of Groups I and VI were alike, and their results were similar. This same pattern seemed to be noted for Groups II and IV and Groups III and V. To check the results, each group repeated the experience with the three jars and the candles and compared their results. This time the average result for Jar A was about 15 seconds, while the candle burned in Jar B for about 5 seconds, and in Jar C about 20 seconds.

The children quickly explained that this was because the candle burned longer in a larger jar. One girl said that Jar A was about three times as large as Jar B. What would happen to the burning time of a candle if they were to use a jar twice the size of Jar A? The certainty of the children's answers clearly illustrates the results of first-hand observations used to construct predictions about future events. These children were using the information of their experience as a basis for going beyond that experience to predicting future events of a similar nature.

Episode 10.4

In a fifth-grade class, pairs of children were busy at work with wires, bulbs, sockets, batteries, and small rectangular boards with six dots on them. Their conversations revealed that they were checking to see which combinations of dots would result in the bulb's lighting. If the bulb would light, then they inferred that the dots were connected behind on the board which they could not see. Why this inference? Earlier, these children had discovered how to light the bulb with two wires and a battery. They had discovered that it would only light when the circuit was complete—with the wire running from the base of the bulb to the top of the battery, and from the bottom of the battery to the side of the bulb base. Whenever the circuit was broken, the bulb did not light. As the children tried out this inference with different boards, they quickly observed that if they compared the results of A–B, B–C, and A–C, and if the bulb burned with those, they could make three different inferences as to how the board must be wired:

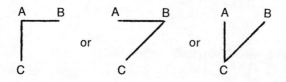

Being able to construct several inferences from the same set of observations was the challenge at which they were working. These children were using the information of their observations to infer what would happen, and then gathering further observational evidence to support or modify their inferences.

Episode 10.5

A murmur of excitement ran through the sixth-grade class. Each child had just received a set of photographs of the surface of the moon. Comments about cheese, squiggly things, and bumps were made and these were followed by more thorough observations when the students were asked to identify the direction from which the light came. Puzzled looks gave way to involved sighs as different ones attempted to support their ideas with descriptions of light and dark spots on the moon photos. Their conversation caused some to want to check on shadows, and others wanted to know how large the holes were, or were they really mountains. After a set of experiences over several days, the children had learned how to measure the size of an object in a photograph by knowing how large it appeared to be in the picture and how far away the camera was when the picture was taken. Then the teacher gave new data on the moon photos—the approximate distance above the moon's surface when the picture was taken. The excitement of being able to describe the actual size of parts of the moon's surface as well as being able to determine the alternative inferences as to the direction of sunlight was matched by the new insights that the children gained about the vastness and emptiness of the moon's surface. Interpreting the second-hand data of moon photos illustrates how children used a variety of measurements to construct and confirm a variety of interpretations of these moon photos.

SCIENCE—A PROCESS APPROACH
WHAT IS IT?

The Scope

There is joy in the search for knowledge; there is excitement in seeing, however limited, into the workings of the physical and biological world; there is intellectual power to be gained in learning the scientist's approach to the solution of human problems. The first task and central purpose of science education is to awaken in the child, whether or not he will become a professional scientist, a sense of the joy, the excitement, and the intellectual power of science. ("Science—A Process Approach," *Commentary for Teachers,* Xerox Education, p. 3.)

So begins the preface to this program in science which was developed under the direction of John Mayor and the Commission on Science Education of the American Association for the Advancement of Science. The entire sequence of activities from kindergarten to sixth grade is based on specific ways in which a scientist processes knowledge.

Each exercise is designed to help a child to acquire a greater sophistication in the skill of the processes of science. As described by the program developers in K–3, the eight processes are:

1. *Observing.* Observing relations under conditions in which one or more physical properties is systematically varied.

2. *Measuring.* Identifying, recognizing, and naming the length, width, volume, temperature, and weight of objects, as well as time intervals, using standard units of measurement. The presentation of measurements is made by means of a bar graph.

3. *Using Number Relationships.* Describing the sum and product of two-digit addition and multiplication by means of verbal and written number sentences.

4. *Using Space/Time Relationships.* Identifying and recognizing the effects of motion as they apply to dimensions of effort, distance, direction, time, and appearance.

5. *Classifying.* Devising classifications of collections of objects by means of single or multiple dimensions such as state of matter, color, volume, symmetry, area, and weight.

6. *Inferring.* Making reasonable inferences from observed events, and distinguishing between an observation and an inference.

7. *Predicting.* Making and testing a prediction of a specific outcome based upon an observed set of events.

8. *Communicating.* Communicating a series of observations from one individual to another by means of one or more of the following: oral and/or written descriptions of changes in the physical state, motion, color, weight, volume, and area; written descriptions of quantitative measurements using standard units of length, area, and volume; presentation of observed data through bar and point graphs.

Other processes are emphasized in grades 4 through 6. These are called the integrated processes of science.

1. *Making operational definitions.* The importance of this activity is apparent to every scientist. For example, if one proposes the hypothesis that learning requires attention, one must then undertake to define both "learning" and "attention" in such a way that another person can identify these events in terms of operations. It is quite unsatisfactory, for example, to say that attention means "mental concentration" (a common student response); this phrase has not been operationally defined. A number of operational definitions of "attention" would be possible; for example, "an individual is attending to a familiar object in a visual scene if he is able to state correctly the presence or absence of the object immediately following the disappearance of the scene." For another example, an operational definition of "mass" is "that property of an object which determines the amount of acceleration that will be imparted to it by force of a given magnitude." Practice in formulating operational definitions of suitable degrees of complexity can be expected to contribute greatly to the student's knowledge of the processes of science.

2. *Formulating hypotheses.* The objective of such instruction is to make the student capable of formulating reasonable hypotheses. He should be able to distinguish the hypothesis he makes from the observations from which it has been drawn, and also from the observations required to test it. The latter requirement implies that the student is able to make operational definitions of the "intervening variables" which form a part of his hypothesis. As the term hypothesis is used in *Science—A Process Approach,* a hypothesis is a general statement. For example, if a pupil has found that a copper wire is a good conductor of electricity, and that it is also a good conductor of heat, he might make the inference that a pair of scissors which is a good conductor of electricity is also a good conductor of heat. He tests this inference and finds that the inference is supported. Then he may state: "All good conductors

of electricity are good conductors of heat." This statement is a hypothesis. Of course he cannot prove that a general statement (a hypothesis) is true, but by conducting many tests he may be able to show that the hypothesis is strongly supported.

3. *Controlling variables.* To a large extent, the student's previous study of science has emphasized the systematic observation of naturally occurring events. But he should then begin to learn that he can make observations under conditions that he deliberately sets out to control and manipulate. For example, if he wishes to study the effect of amount of light on plant growth, he must plan deliberately to place a set of identical plants under conditions in which other variables are deliberately kept constant, and light is deliberately varied. Obviously, this kind of activity grows out of his previous learning about systematic observation, and leads into the performance of experiments.

4. *Interpreting data.* The proper interpretation of data, in ways which will at once get the most out of them, and at the same time avoid over-generalizing, is another important scientific activity. A background for the learning of acceptable performance in date interpretation has been provided by previous experience in inference and communication, as well as by the substantial learning of concretely based concepts. We should like the student to be able to draw imaginative and comprehensive conclusions which are unsupported by data, or which fail to take account of alternative explanations.

5. *Experimenting.* The planning, execution, and communicating of simple experiments is surely not too much to expect of children who have had the advantage of the process approach to the learning of science. However, simple experiments are not easy to design, since they can so easily go beyond the store of knowledge possessed by the child. The attempt to get the student involved in experimentation nevertheless deserves to be made. There must be some amount of structuring of these experiments, if the learning they generate is to be of dependable value. It is a challenge to the designer of such exercises to avoid the "cook book" character of old fashioned "laboratory

work," while at the same time requiring the student to formulate the problem, think out his procedure, make his observations, and draw his conclusions." *

To develop in children the desired competencies in using the processes of science, a setting of science content is used to cover various dimensions in the biological and behavioral sciences, the physical sciences, and mathematics.

Science Content **

Describing the role of content in the development of a process, the developers of this program state:

The primary goal of *Science—A Process Approach* is to develop in children competence in the process of science. This competence is developed in a setting of science content and concepts drawn from many fields of science.

The Biological and Behavioral Sciences

In their earliest school experiences children are introduced to living things and things that have been living. The introduction is much more than seeing them and naming them. The children learn to identify similarities and differences in living things and those that have been living, using these similarities and differences to classify them, and then to describe them so that another child can readily identify the object they are describing. These abilities provide a solid basis for later more detailed study of interactions of living things with their environments. In *Science—A Process Approach* children become acquainted with a multitude of living things such as leaves, nuts, shells, animals and plants in an aquarium, and animals and plants in their natural environment or that

* *The Psychological Basis of Science—A Process Approach,* AAAS Miscellaneous Publication, 65–8, pp. 29–31. Reprinted by permission of the AAAS.
** *Commission on Science Education Newsletter,* Vol. 5, No. 2 (July 1969), pp. 7–8.

can be brought into the classroom or that can be studied in pictures. They begin to see what distinguishes living from nonliving objects around them. Living things eat, grow, reproduce, and move about freely. The children describe their color, their size, their shape, their symmetry or lack of it, their odor, and how they move about. Soon they are able to describe changes in living things, such as color changes that occur in plant leaves, the movement of a potted plant in response to sunlight, or the response of sensitive plants to touch or heat.

Later the children investigate modes of living and behavior of animals by observing the growth of young animals, reactions of fish to various stimuli, maze-learning by guinea pigs, and responses of brine shrimp. They use microscopes to observe leaves, algae, insect wings, and animal tissues. They grow mold gardens and compare rates of growth of different mold colonies. They investigate transpiration of water from plants and growth of plants from seeds and plant parts.

Some aspects of human behavior and physiology are included in the science content of the program. The children measure their own rates of reaction to various stimuli, their perceptual judgment in viewing optical illusions, and the resolving power of their eyes. They count pulse beats and measure the volume of air they exhale in a measured period of time. An introduction to genetics is made in two exercises. One is concerned with tasters and nontasters of PTC paper, and the other with the morphology of drosophila in the F_1 and F_2 generations of a cross between normal and vestigial-winged flies.

The Physical Sciences

Science content from the physical sciences includes several exercises at different grade levels on the properties of solids, liquids, and gases. At an early age the children observe and describe color, shape, size, texture, and odor of solid objects. Later they use these and other properties in identifying minerals. Observing solids changing to liquids and collecting air by displacement of water introduces the children to the liquid and gaseous phases of matter. Later they compare the compressibility of solids, liquids, and gases and still later investigate quantitatively the relationship between the volume of an enclosed gas and the pressure applied to it.

The children begin to observe changes in properties in kindergarten where they observe the change in color of Congo red paper when it is put into an acid. Later they observe the color of red cabbage in acidic and basic solutions. They observe gas production, solubility, and color change as they mix various white solids with liquids, and they use the information they collect to identify unknown solids and liquids.

Other content from the physical sciences includes magnetism, electric circuits, and simple optics.

A number of concepts basic to all science appear in many places in the program. Among these are concepts of force, inertia, temperature, heat, mass, and density.

Mathematics

One of the science processes in the program is Using Numbers. The mathematics content of this part of the program starts with the concept of sets and their members and then progresses to order properties of whole numbers, counting, and numerals. Negative integers and addition of positive and negative integers are introduced with the number line. As needed, multiplication, division, and decimals are introduced, in every case at an earlier age than in the usual school mathematics program.

The program contains geometric topics, including symmetry, measurement of angles and two-dimensional projections and sections of three-dimensional figures.

The mathematics topics culminate with probability, including its application to genetic problems such as the inheritance of the ability to taste PTC paper.

The Sequence

While each exercise is designed to assist a child in acquiring a specific skill within the context of science content, there is a specific order to the exercises. With each of the science processes, the individual skills are identified. These skills were placed in a logical order from simple to complex. By testing children, it was then possible to arrange these learning skills from simple to complex, based on what seemed both logically correct in science and psychologically accurate for most children. Thus, each activity is designed to help children acquire the skill necessary for the next step in the learning process.

Science—A Process Approach is a non-graded program in which there are seven levels. At each level there are about 20 exercises or short units.

The exercise is the unit of interest to the teacher. It is part of the Teacher's Guide. For each exercise the following items are included:

Number: Measuring 8	This means it is the eighth exercise in the sequence of the process of measuring.
Title: Measuring Forces with Springs	The title identifies the context in science on which the exercise will be based.
Objectives	The objectives are stated in terms of what the child should be able to do by the end of the exercise.
Sequence	This identifies which exercises should have preceded and which ones will follow the lesson, based on the science content or process skills which are the focus of the exercise.

The *rationale* describes the reason for the exercise to come at this time in the science experience of the child. It often includes specific explanations of science concepts which teachers have found essential, such as the definition of force.

Vocabulary identifies words that the child should be able to use by the end of the exercise, such as:

scale   weight

spring   earth–pull

force   counterbalance

Materials

Since the need for first-hand experience with a variety of materials in a variety of situations is essential, the materials are an important part of the program. These materials are usually supplied by a commercial distributor in drawers or kits.

Instructional Procedure

The introduction is a setting in which it is possible for the teacher to determine the children's general readiness for this experience and to assess their interest in the task. The "Instructional Activities" describe both tasks and suggested questions or ways the teacher can guide children in acquiring the skills described in the objectives.

The "Generalizing Experience" is an opportunity for children to use the capabilities described in the objectives in a new setting.

To help the teacher and children know when they are ready for a new experience, the *appraisal activity* is an evaluation activity for the group, whereas the *competency measure* is designed as an individual measure of how well the child has acquired the objectives of the exercise.

TO TEACH *SCIENCE—A PROCESS APPROACH*

What the child can do—his behavior—is the key focus of the program. In planning to teach an exercise, it is our opinion that the *first step* that you should complete is to carefully read the objectives and picture what the child who has acquired those behaviors will do. It is helpful to write out a specific task that illustrates a child's doing each of these behaviors. Then it is helpful to check the appraisal and competency measure for other illustrations of such tasks.

The *second step* is to carefully read the activity and make a brief outline of what the children will be doing in each activity.

The *third step* is to review the activities outlined in the second step. Identify which of the objectives is the focus of each activity. You may have more than one activity for each objective but you should have at least one activity for each objective. A special note of caution is important. In many activities, you will observe a variety of children's behavior. The learning experience for the child will be much more useful if the activity has a clear focus on a single objective rather than a vague mixture of many objectives.

The *fourth step* is essential. For an activity to come alive, you will need material and equipment. For each activity, identify what material and equipment will be needed and where you will likely be able to secure it.

It is very difficult for you to direct someone to a place you have never been. If you have been there, you can give much more specific directions and you can anticipate problems the other person might experience in his seeking the place for which he is looking. This is a key point in *step five*. Do the activities yourself *before* initiating them in your classroom.

In your planning, decisions about space and time are an essential *sixth step*. Look back at each activity. Estimate how much class time will be needed by the children to complete each activity. Mentally picture how you will arrange the room for individual work, for small or team group interaction, or for total group discussion.

WHY A PROCESS APPROACH TO SCIENCE INSTRUCTION?

The answer to this question is contained in the statement of the purpose and objectives for science education in schools. This was written by William Kessen, "Science as Enquiry," *Commentary for Teachers*.

Science is best taught as a procedure of enquiry. Just as reading is a fundamental instrument for exploring whatever may be written, so science is a fundamental instrument for exploring whatever may be tested by observation and experiment. Science is more than a body of facts, a collection of principles, and a set of machines for measurement; it is a structured and directed way of asking and answering questions. It is no mean pedagogical feat to teach a child the facts of science and technology; it is a pedagogical triumph to teach him these facts in their relation to the procedures of scientific enquiry. And the intellectual gain is far greater than the child's ability to conduct a chemical experiment or to discover some of the characteristics of static electricity. The procedures of scientific enquiry, learned not as a canon of rules but as ways of finding answers, can be applied without limit. The well-taught child will approach human behavior and social structure and the claims of authority with the same spirit of alert skepticism that he adopts toward scientific theories. It is here that the future citizen who will not become a scientist will learn that science is not memory or magic but rather a disciplined form of human curiosity.

That science is "more than a body of facts" is widely accepted by both teachers and teacher educators. Defining that "more" is the point of uniqueness to *Science—A Process Approach*. In a somewhat lengthy statement, however, the developers of *Science —A Process Approach* have shared their view in an elegant and convincing argument. They describe the procedures of science as:

Scientific problems arise in the life of children just as they arise in the guided exploration of scientists. Astonishment in the presence of natural beauty, surprise—even frustration—at the failure of a prediction, and the demand for sense in the face of confusion are the beginnings of scientific enquiry. But how do we then proceed?

Among the most demanding of scientific tasks and certainly among the most difficult to teach is the statement of a problem. Is there a meaningful question to be asked? What techniques should be used to answer it? How does one go about making a prediction or developing a hypothesis? As he asks these questions, the student begins to learn how active enquiry can lead to testable questions and eventually to the solution of problems. He is introduced also to the pleasures and problems of inventive thought—of considering what might be as well as what is.

There are many ways to answer a provocative question in science and the child should come to recognize that he must adapt his method to the problem in hand. As he runs against different problems, the child will learn to use several sources of reliable information—observation, experiment, books, museums, and informed adults.

Whatever the problem, the child's ability to observe should be extended so that he understands the wide range of observations possible even when simple phenomena are under study. He must learn to order the evidence of his senses.

Attention to the complex activity of comparison of phenomena will introduce the child to an essential task in science—the perception of differences and similarities among events.

The child will use his ability to observe and to compare in building systems of classification and in recognizing their usefulness and their limitations in science.

The child should learn to use the instruments of science. As he studies these instruments, the teacher is given an opportunity to instruct the child in measurement. He will learn when it is wise to estimate a measurement and when precision is required; he will learn the importance of agreement among observers and the relations among different systems of measurement.

The use of laboratory techniques—especially the experiment—deserves special attention. The experiment is the sharpest tool of science and in devising an experiment the child exercises his ability to pose a question, to consider possible answers, to select appropriate instruments, to make careful measurements, and to be aware of sources of error. It is unlikely that children in the first years of school will manage well all aspects of sound laboratory procedure but the best lessons of the experiment can be taught only to the child who is actively engaged with the equipment and procedures of the laboratory. The teacher must adapt his desire for precision to the child's excitement in the search; a premature demand for exactness in experimental manipulation may blunt the student's commitment and pleasure.

After the problem is posed, the data gathered, and a hypothesis developed, the science student must evaluate evidence and draw conclusions. Sometimes this is a simple step; sometimes it involves the review and modification of the entire plan with renewed attention to problem, to hypothesis, and to data–protocols. The goal is to make sense of the data and the pursuit of this goal will, on occasion, lead to the detection of an error or to the design of another study. It may also lead to the invention of a model or theory through which we can comprehend data.

Throughout the course of science education the need to communicate is present. Describing a bird to his class, graphing a mathematical function, writing an experimental paper—experience with each mode of report is essential to the development of the science student.

The child's ability to communicate in science will both depend on and contribute to the solution of this most general problem of the curriculum—accurate and effective communication.

The procedures of science described here in the context of early science education are recognizably the procedures of science at all levels of sophistication. Scientific enquiry is a seamless fabric. The content will change, the demand for precision will vary, the generality of conclusion will be different, the interrelation of studies will be understood in different ways; but the procedures and attitudes of scientific study remain remarkably the same from the time the kindergarten child wonders about color to the time the graduate physicist wonders about particle emission.*

The development of *Science—A Process Approach* has extended over a number of years starting with 1961. From the *Com-*

* From *Commentary for Teachers*. (New York: Xerox Education, 1970), pp. 4–5.

mentary for Teachers, a resource book for teachers, the chronology of its development is as follows: *

1961

A feasibility study (sponsored by the American Association for the Advancement of Science with support of the National Science Foundation) brought scientists, educational administrators, and teachers together to consider the preparation of science materials for elementary and junior high schools by teams of teachers and scientists. Conferences were held in St. Louis, Berkeley, and Washington. Participants in the conferences urged that a national commission be appointed to work with several centers in planning and developing instructional materials for pre-high school science and to give direction to a large-scale coordinated attack on problems of science education. A report of the feasibility study was published in *Science,* June 23, 1961, Vol. 133, No. 3469, 2019–2024.

Spring and Summer 1962

The American Association for the Advancement of Science appointed a Commission on Science Education, which sponsored two eight-day conferences, one at Cornell University in June and the other at the University of Wisconsin in August. Scientists, teachers, and school administrators came together at these conferences to consider the impact of the new high school science courses, to review research in science education and in learning, and to seek ways of improving science education in elementary and junior high schools. The conferences recommended that the Commission sponsor the development of instructional materials beginning at the kindergarten level, and that these materials stress the processes of science.

* From *Commentary for Teachers.* (New York: Xerox Education, 1970) pp. 293–96.

1962–63

A panel prepared a statement of purposes and objectives of science education in school, and a review of research in science education was published. The Commission staff formulated plans for the development of a science program for the primary grades, and with the help of scientists, science educators, and teachers prepared preliminary outlines of course materials.

Summer 1963

At Stanford University in an eight-week summer writing session, thirty-five scientists and elementary school teachers wrote 100 exercises for use in primary grades. Competency measures were prepared to be used by "tryout teachers" to report pupil achievement. A Teacher's Guide was also prepared. After staff editing, these materials were published as *Science—A Process Approach,* Parts One through Five, Experimental Edition, prepared for testing in elementary schools. The writers worked in close proximity to the School Mathematics Study Group which advised them on the preparation of mathematics exercises needed in the science program. Whenever possible, the writers tried out drafts of exercises in demonstration classes.

1963–64

The experimental edition prepared in the summer of 1963 was tried in twelve centers by 106 "tryout teachers" with approximately 3000 children. A science consultant and a coordinator assigned to each "tryout center" helped orient the teachers and assisted in other ways. The teachers submitted a feedback form and scores on competency measures after each exercise.

Summer 1964

Again at Stanford University, fifty scientists and teachers, working for eight weeks, revised the materials prepared in the summer of 1963 and wrote additional exercises and competency measures. The Teacher's Guide was extended for publication as a Commentary for Teachers. After staff editing, the revised and new exercises were published as *Science—A Process Approach,* Parts One through Six, Second Experimental Edition.

1964–65

Parts One through Six of *Science—A Process Approach* were tried out by eighteen teachers in kindergarten through grade 5 in each of fourteen centers. Approximately 7000 children studied the program—some new to the program and others in the second year. Again, center consultants and coordinators directed work in the "tryout centers," and "tryout teachers" submitted feedback forms and scores on competency measures for each exercise.

Summer 1965

Fifty scientists and teachers worked at Michigan State University for eight weeks on the revision of the Second Experimental Edition of *Science—A Process Approach.* Thirty new exercises for Parts Six and Seven were written and all of the earlier materials were revised. After staff editing, the materials were published as the Third Experimental Edition of *Science—A Process Approach,* Parts One through Seven. Booklets containing competency measures for each exercise in the seven parts and the first edition of the Science Process Instrument, a device for testing the progress of an individual child through the process hierarchies, were printed. The Commentary for Teachers was revised and extended.

During one week of the summer writing session, two key representatives from each "tryout center" came to a teacher-education conference to try out and evaluate an in-service program for teachers. The objective was to enlist assistance from the field in identifying and dealing effectively with problems teachers face in teaching science to children by the process approach.

1965–66

Each of the fourteen "tryout centers" assigned additional teachers in the intermediate grades (4, 5, and 6) to *Science—A Process Approach,* and fewer primary teachers took part. Some of the children were in the program for the third, some for the second, and others for the first year. The "tryout teachers" continued to submit competency measure reports and their evaluations of the exercises on revised feedback forms. The Science Process Instrument was tried in several of the centers, both with children in *Science—A Process Approach* classes and in classes with another science program. Center consultants and teachers also reported on their experiences in the in-service education program. A two-day conference of center consultants and "tryout teachers" was held in Washington, D.C. in January.

Summer 1966

At the University of Maryland, thirty-five teachers and scientists revised Parts Five, Six, and Seven of the Third Experimental Edition of *Science—A Process Approach,* the competency measures, the Commentary for Teachers and the in-service program, and the Science Process Instrument. Additional competency measures were written as group tests for use in intermediate grades. A second conference for teachers from the tryout centers and for representatives of school systems using *Science—A Process Approach* at their own expense (not official "tryout centers") convened for eight days during the writing session. Again, the teacher education materials were tried out, and the effects of the program on teachers were measured.

Most of the writers worked for five weeks, with about one-third of them remaining for two additional weeks. After staff editing, the materials produced in the summer were published as Parts Five, Six, and Seven, the First Revision of the Third Experimental Edition. Revised editions of the competency measures and Commentary for Teachers were published.

1966-67

Eighty-five percent of the 112 tryout teachers in fourteen centers were teaching in the intermediate grades. Most of the centers also included one third-grade teacher. "Tryout teachers" continued to meet in in-service sessions with a science consultant. At a two-day conference in Washington in the spring, they reported on and compared teaching experiences. They also reported competency measure scores and feedback comments on each exercise taught. During this year, films were made of classes in the University of Chicago Laboratory Schools and in Monmouth, Illinois.

Xerox Corporation was selected to further develop the materials of *Science—A Process Approach* and to produce and market the entire program in the United States and its territories. Xerox published Parts A, B, and C (formerly called Parts One, Two, and Three) in late spring, together with a Hierarchy Chart covering the behavioral hierarchies for the basic processes. Xerox also made available kits of materials for all parts of the program.

Summer 1967

Twenty-four scientists and teachers met in a six-week writing session at the University of Maryland to revise Parts Six and Seven of *Science—A Process Approach,* and various evaluation instruments. Copy was prepared for the Second Edition of the Guide for In-service Instruction with booklets of Response Sheets and two forms of the Process Measure for Teachers to be used in in-service classes. Conferences were held at several universities to assist teachers who were planning to teach the program, to inform school administrators about the program, and to train teachers of in-service programs.

1967-68

Parts Six and Seven, Fourth Experimental Edition, were published in the fall. Tryout of these two revised Parts was continued in eleven centers by 48 "tryout teachers." A number of fourth-grade teachers tried out a final revision of Part Five as prepared for the AAAS–Xerox edition. The Commission staff prepared copy for the monograph, An Evaluation Model and Its Application, Second Report, published in April; revised the Commentary for Teachers; and prepared the final revision of the Hierarchy Chart for the basic processes. Part D (formerly Part Four) was published by Xerox in late spring.

Summer 1968

Several scientists and teachers joined with the staff to revise Parts Six and Seven following the tryout of the Fourth Experimental Edition. Others served as consultants to and members of a joint AAAS–Xerox committee in preparing copy for the Xerox publication of the first part of the Guide for In-service Instruction and prepared copy for an extension of the Guide to include Parts Five through Seven.

Summer 1968–69

Xerox published Part E (formerly Part Five) in the fall. The staff conducted further validation studies of the Science Process Instrument. New elements of revised Parts Six and Seven were tried and reported on by experienced tryout teachers. After a final review of tryout suggestions, these Parts were submitted to Xerox. The Commission staff prepared final copy for the Commentary for Teachers.

Index

Index